STANDING ON SHAMSAN

STANDING ON SHAMSAN

Garry Kilworth

HarperCollins
An Imprint of HarperCollins*Publishers*

HarperCollins*Publishers*
77–85 Fulham Palace Road
Hammersmith, London W6 8JB

Published by HarperCollins*Publishers* 1992

1 3 5 7 9 8 6 4 2

A catalogue record for this book
is available from the British Library

ISBN 0 246 13895 5

Set in Linotron Ehrhardt by Intype, London

Printed in Great Britain by
HarperCollinsManufacturing Glasgow

*To those Aden friends of my childhood,
especially Rosemary and Max.*

Lord, what fools these mortals be!

A Midsummer Night's Dream,
Shakespeare

Prologue

In 1839 an obscure British sea captain by the name of Haines sailed into the harbour of a poor Arab fishing village and claimed it as the first of Queen Victoria's overseas possessions. A local sultan took exception to the occupation and engaged the British marines on the shore. The Arabs were beaten and eventually the sultan signed a lease allowing the British to use the village as a coaling station.

The small village was situated on the tip of the south-west Arabian peninsula, and might have remained a strip of beach covered in rotting fishheads for a long time to come, perhaps indefinitely, had not a colonial power been interested in the position it commanded over the Red Sea and Indian Ocean.

One hundred and ten years later that same Arab village had been transformed into the second busiest harbour in the world after New York. The British were once good at taking sparsely inhabited inlets, and turning them into rich industrious harbours. What they were not so good at was recognizing changes in political climates and the fact that if you create something on foreign soil there will come a time when you have to leave it. This may be done violently, it may be done peacefully, it may be done willingly, it may even be done gracefully, but it is rarely done correctly. Perhaps there is no right way to leave a piece of land occupied by force of arms?

At the time of the first British occupation, the landscape around the village, beyond the giant extinct volcanic crater, was thickly forested. Mimosa, tamarisk, camel's thorn and myrrh shrubs grew

1

abundantly and were populated by rabbits, hares and gazelles; foxes and hyenas; doves, pigeons, storks and herons; ducks and flamingoes. By the mid-1800s the land had been deforested by the successors of Captain Haines, to build houses, ships and other things necessary to the creation of a great port.

The village was one hundred and eighty miles from an ancient city once known as Sheba, the home of King Solomon's regal visitor Queen Bilquis who reputedly returned to Sheba with his child. The boy child's descendants became the emperors of Ethiopia. The people of Sheba were descended from Qahtan, the Joktan of the Bible's Genesis. Today that city, known now as Sana, rises out of a tall plateau as a continuation of the red stone on which it stands, into which it is built. It has the appearance of having grown out of the rock, as though the cliffs have bloomed into a geometrical flower, the petals of which are sandstone houses and the rigid stamens, gold-tipped minarets. A sort of cubist fairy-tale city with tall narrow Arabesque dwellings, fused together, decorated with latticework windows and multiple-arched balconies that look out over the desert from their high foundations. In the 1950s its Imam rulers were cruel and barbarous, and the country had not been permitted to progress beyond a medieval society.

Between Sana, the capital of the Yemen, and the fishing village that grew into a prosperous port, was a wilderness, a wedge of desert called the Hadhramaut, ruled by sheiks and peopled by wild tribes that remained lawless at least until the mid-1900s.

Summer temperatures in the village rarely fell below 32 degrees Celsius and the winter was just five degrees cooler. It was a sweltering place which most humans would have rejected out of hand as a place of habitation. When it became a busy harbour the heat and humidity of course remained, though the population grew from just over a thousand, to a quarter of a million.

In 1967 the colonial power withdrew, harried until the end by Marxist republicans eager to oust the builders of empires and

2

call the place by another name: the independent republic of South Yemen.

That piece of parched sand and rock, with its fierce sun, its flies, its pi-dogs and buzzards, its sharks and barracudas, was the home of my adolescence. I love it as dearly as a Highlander his Scottish hills, as deeply as a Welshman his valleys. It became part of me. It was my growing place, my corner of the earth, closer to me than the land of my birth. I cared nothing, nor do I care, for politics or nationalities, who rules or controls, what name or flag covers its face. Those who served there, who lived there as colonials, can never feel the same about it as a child raised in its dust. What was once a poor fishing village is in my soul.

The name of the village was Aden.

The village began its colonial life as a coaling station for British ships on their way to India: the Empire fuelling the Empire. The images that coal produces seem appropriate to a place like Aden: slag heaps, furnaces, dust and grime. Aden in the winter is hot and dusty. Aden in the summer is unbearably hot and insufferably dusty. The rocky backdrop of Crater throws the heat down on to the town of Tawahi, or Steamer Point as the British called it, and within the volcano itself the original town of Adan is twice as hot as its external neighbour. An opening on the seaward side allows some breezes to enter the cone, but four-fifths of Adan is surrounded by high igneous rock walls decorated with fortifications from another era. On the landward side, there is the main entrance to Crater, barely the width of a road. Colonial children used to climb up above the gap, oblivious of the blazing sun, and watch the traffic hustling for space as camel carts and Morris Oxfords squeezed past each other in the narrow space below.

There is an oasis of sorts, not far from Crater, called Sheik Othman Gardens, where date palms and coconut trees and

3

oleander and other shrubs grow in a parkland of coarse grass. Between the Gardens and Crater lie the saltpans, set out in square fields, which are covered with seawater left to evaporate. Before the salt is collected the squares glisten with crushed diamonds under the bright eastern sun.

The rest of Aden State is just sand. Some of it black, some of it a dirty grey, but most of it sandy sand. Reaching above it all, the great jagged claw which is the peak of Jebel Shamsan.

1

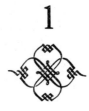

The gulli-gulli man came on board ship at Port Said. Dix and I had been up since dawn, watching the misty shore as we steamed into harbour aboard the SS *Dunera*, a troopship that was taking both us and our families to Aden, where our fathers were stationed. My father was a sergeant armourer in the Royal Air Force and had been one of those pawns in an ill-fated attempt to teach the Egyptians whose canal it was that cut through their land. When this failed, my dad was sent further down the Red Sea, to the Aden Protectorate. Shortly after he arrived he sent for us.

While the day was still cool, the bumboats came from shore, to sell their wares to the service families, some of whom had only a vague idea where Egypt was and had never seen an Arab. The bumboats were open dinghies displaying all kinds of exotic paraphernalia, from bullwhips to music boxes to ivory carvings. The Arab traders tossed a cork-weighted line up to the deck of the ship and when you pulled on this line a basket came up. Another line was attached to the other side of the basket. In this way money and goods were seesawed back and forth between the bumboats and the passengers, while brown-skinned boys with dark eyes dived for coins thrown down into the water. I had a Brownie box camera and was taking pictures of everything from the giant Johnnie Walker man, top-hatted, tail-coated, pantalooned and striding over the flat white roofs of Port Said with his silver-knobbed stick in his hand – to the feluccas with their sharp triangular sails cutting like shark fins amongst the liners.

Dix kept springing up in front of me just as I was about to click the camera.

"Whaaa!" he shouted, his hair flopping over his eyes. "Another picture of the missing link. You'll soon have enough for a chain."

"Bloody hell, Dix!" I cried. "You're wasting my film. I've only got twelve shots."

"Don't swear at me," he said, mildly.

Jack Dickenson was thirteen years old, six months older than I was, with a magnificent build for a boy of his age. He wore round tortoiseshell glasses, the kind they used to hand out on the National Health, and had square features. Somewhere in his background a German ancestor stood, stolid and firm, though Dix never would have admitted it. The Second World War had been over for only a handful of years at that time.

I was much slimmer than Dix, but wiry, with fair curly hair and looks which ran into prettiness, though I would have attacked anyone who dared to say so with flailing fists. I had two younger brothers who were more distant from my world than Palaeolithic Man. The next one down was three years younger and unreachable in terms of making any sort of relationship. The only time I used them for company was when we were changing locations, one of the frequent hazards of belonging to a service family, and had no other friends. This was a mutual arrangement, since I could no more fit into their lives than they could into mine, except during emergencies. I conversed with them only to exchange comics. *Captain Marvel, Superman, Batman and Robin* transcended any difference in age, from six to sixteen, and beyond. We were also into a certain amount of culture, improving our education with Classic Comics, which retold stories like *Doctor Jekyll and Mr Hyde* with much more colour and excitement than any novel.

I also read Richmal Crompton's "William" books, Agatha Christie, and novels like *Kim*, but my siblings didn't know about my liking for books without pictures and I think they would have been shocked to learn I read such things outside the classroom.

6

"How about one with me by the funnel?" said Dix, swaggering towards the centre of the ship.

"I got six with you by the funnel," I complained, "one of them upside-down."

Dix was very athletic and could stand on his head or walk on his hands. I was tremendously impressed by this and not a little jealous.

Just at that moment there was a commotion further down the deck and children began running past us.

"What's up?" cried Dix, grabbing a kid by the collar.

"Gulli-gulli man," shouted the boy into his face, and then squirming out of his grasp, he ran on. "Gulli-gulli man's come."

"Who's he?" I asked Dix.

Dix had been this route before, when he was eight years old, down through the canal and along the East African coast, to Rhodesia. Dix had lived in Bulawayo, had walked with lions, run through the legs of elephants, stalked springbok and had dug jiggers out of his toes with a needle. Dix knew the grasslands, the thorn trees of Africa. Dix had known black tribesmen with stained teeth, who could pin a feather to a tree with a spear. Dix could sing a song that began, *"There's forty thousand yarpies in the old Transvaal . . . "* and explain to you over and over again that a yarpie was an Afrikaner. Dix knew that a certain snake was called a boa-constrictor, not a boa-constructor as I had believed.

Dix was a bloody show-off and I hated him sometimes, especially when he was bragging about his life in Bulawayo.

"The magic man!" he cried, and we ran along the deck to where a man in dirty scarlet robes was in the process of removing a dove from a boy's nose.

The gulli-gulli man was lean and brown, with a huge hooked nose, under which curved a scimitar grin. He was straight out of a story: *The Thousand and One Nights* or *The Thief of Baghdad*. His tricks were the tricks of any sleight-of-hand magician, but his flair was so much more. He produced coins out of his nose, birds out of his ears, silk handkerchief ropes out of his mouth.

7

He was an Aladdin's cave of small treasures. No heart, no liver or kidneys, no lungs, no backbone or ribs, no sternum: only a cavity full of silver coins, ring-necked doves and coloured fabric. He coughed them up, he sneezed them out.

"A grand piano next," whispered Dix.

The gulli-gulli man's hair crackled with magic: his black eyes sparkled with mysticism. On his head was a red fez. There were strange guttural words uttered before each wondrous illusion. He wrapped things in newspapers covered in Arabic writing and they changed inside their parcels. Different objects were revealed on unwrapping the same sheets. With three copper beakers he defied the adults who thought they could follow his rapid hand-movements and pinpoint under which cup was the small white ball. Little yellow chicks appeared amongst us, under our grey flannel shirts, all chirrups and fluff.

With the coming of the gulli-gulli man a change took place within me. I knew that from that moment on the world would be a more fascinating place. The sky was now a deep blue, the sea now a deep green. They were no longer the wishy-washy imitations of each other that they had been on the East Anglian coast. One could define an horizon.

No more squashed school assemblies in the dusty halls of Felixstowe primary and secondary schools, where the smell of yesterday's afters, usually rhubarb and custard, drifted above the floor as thick as marsh mist. At these solemn gatherings hymns were browned in the ovens of lower-class lungs before delivery: *"An did them feet, in aynshunt tyme... "* I remember singing for those in peril on the sea and for rain to swell the grain, for Christian soldiers to march onward to war, for the pilgrim prepared to vanquish giants and lions. Hymns by the hundred. They remained in my blood and burst forth in moments of well-being. And at Christmas-time, the carols, *"Earth stood hard as iron, water like a stone... "* Carols with beautiful Christina Rossetti words. Songs that were, like the times-tables I learned by rote, so deeply part of me they must have been included in the genetic information contained in my DNA. Times-tables, hymns and the Lord's Prayer.

There were only a few religious songs I distrusted. Top of the list was "Once in Royal David's City" which has lines like, *"Christian children all must be, mild, obedient, good as He."* Clearly this was blatant adult propaganda.

All this I thought I had left behind in grey England.

No more classrooms where the fire was a million miles away, warming the pants or skirts of feared antique misters or ma'ams.

No more stubs of chalk, or worse still blackboard dusters, whizzing through the air when I was not paying attention.

No more staring wistfully at a faded shaft of sunlight coming from a dirty skylight up near where God was supposed to live.

In primary school I had learned very little except that the trees at the edge of the playground were Scots pine and their amber sap could be moulded into interesting shapes.

There were some things about England that I would miss. Fishing for newts in the streams, playing around Felixstowe harbour, making French arrows. Dens in the marshes and gang fights in the docklands. Butlin's fairground. None of your studying Latin or French lessons for us. Ours was a lower-class distortion of such time-wasting fripperies. *Horses' doovers, silver plates, murky buckets.* No gentlemen we, though we had our own family rituals to observe:

"What's this?" a bending of my ear, "I sent you upstairs for a wash, not a lick and a promise."

"Ow, I thought I'd scrubbed them, Mum."

"Thought? You know what Thought did? Followed a dustcart and thought it was a wedding. Go back and wash those ears properly."

These, and many other set pieces, were used time and time again, surpassing even clichés in their usage, yet they were comforting to the users, a language that meant everything was all right in the family. The words meant nothing in themselves, but

9

were carrier phrases, bearing an unspoken watchman's message: *"Don't worry, the family is safe. All's well, all's well."*

Mum was very strict on table manners: the sort of behaviour she believed would be found at middle- and upper-class meals, and just in case we were ever asked to the Lord Mayor's Banquet she taught us how to use a seven-course table setting, so we wouldn't let her down. Where she had learned which cutlery to use with what course even mystified our father, but maybe it was in her blood, a natural knowledge, for there was a family myth (despite the fact that our forbears could be traced back for centuries, revealing only sea fishermen and farm labourers) that my grandfather was the bastard son of a union between a gypsy and a member of Sherborne Castle's aristocracy. We could if we liked, we were told, go to the castle and look at the family portraits, for the proof of our antecedents. Uncle Phil was the spit of one of those pictures and me and my brothers had the nose and eyes of another. The gypsy bit we never disputed, for there were dark heads, black eyes, and sallow skins in the family. The aristocracy part we took with a pinch of salt though, of course, there was Mum's knowledge of silverware to take into account before dismissing the claim completely.

Aside from all this, I was proud to come from earthy, seagoing sets of families. They were all good honest yeomen, and true (all except Uncle Dave, who was a crook and spent much of his life in the Scrubs, but he was a black sheep) and could tell the difference between yarrow and fennel, a running sea and a rolling swell. These, in the right places, were more valuable than Latin or French, or the nuances of fine manners.

So I thought, but then I should know what Thought did, my mother having told me often enough.

We left Port Said and began our journey along the Suez Canal, to the Red Sea. The very same waters that Moses had parted, with a little help from God. When we were halfway through the canal the Captain got a message from another troopship, the SS *Windrush*, which had caught fire in the middle of the Mediter-

10

ranean. Someone had been careless with a cigarette end. He informed us over the tannoy that he had been asked if he could assist in picking up survivors, but that we were going on because we could not turn around now we were in the canal. Dix and I thought this was a shame.

"We could have been in on the rescue," said Dix, leaning out of the cabin porthole we had been ordered never to open.

"What can you see?" I asked.

"Nuthin' 'cept a lot of people working in the fields," he complained, "all wrapped up and nowhere to go."

We felt a little guilty too, because when the ship had been in the Bay of Biscay we had played with a tin shaving mug in the showers. The force of the shower water was considerable and we found that by putting the mug underneath it made a hell of a racket. The noise, we realized later, was not unlike that of a fire bell sounding off. When we left the showers there were passengers running everywhere, donning life jackets and asking who was supposed to go to which muster station. My mother grabbed me and Dix's mother grabbed him.

"Get into your life jackets," they yelled at us. "Didn't you hear the fire alarm? Good heavens, it was so loud we couldn't hear ourselves think!"

We did as we were told, sheepishly, and kept our mouths shut. The whole episode remained a mystery to the crew, and no doubt even today there is some hoary old ex-sailor who spins a yarn in the pub about ghost bells sounding off one evening in the Bay of Biscay, a chilling prelude to a disaster that occurred on board another ship not one week later in the Med. Sailors love premonitions.

We passed Port Suez and went on into the Red Sea. It was a magnificent stretch of water, a very deep blue, with lots of strange creatures to watch. We saw manta rays as big as dining-room tabletops gliding beneath us, and porpoise sliding their backs into the sunlight. This was the first time that I realized the sea was another world, just as valid as our own, with strange inhabitants

11

that visited us rarely, and then merely to pass silently by. There were the sharks, intent and purposeful, on their way to an urgent appointment with death. There were clouds of colourful jellyfish, quite the opposite, drifting with no apparent aim or goal. The decks of the *Dunera* were covered in flying fish every morning – beautiful creatures like stranded sea fairies – where they had tried to leap the ship and had struck something or fallen halfway. Their delicate transparent fins reflected all the colours of the sun and sea.

But the stretch of water was endless for the adults, who sickened and all but died on games of canasta or whist, or deck quoits. Dix, daft as he was, played a game with bored passengers. He would find some wistful soul leaning over the rail, eyes fixed on the sharp horizon separating hard from soft blue.

"Land! Over there," he would yell, pointing.

"Where?" would come the animated response.

"Just out of sight," Dix would cry, and take to his heels.

Dix was pathetic sometimes.

2

There were no terrible storms in the Red Sea, as there had been in the Atlantic. The sun shone every day and summer promised to stay for ever. The closer we came to the Gulf of Aden, the happier grew most of the wives, some of whom had not seen their husbands for a year or more. An impromptu party developed one evening when we were four days from our destination, which ended with half of them tipsy and in a long line across the deck singing "Knees-up Mother Brown". For some reason Mum and her friends, especially after a few drinks, loved to sing this song, which has that strange bloodcurdling line *". . . and if I catch you bending, I'll saw your legs right off"*. They exchanged wicked elfin grins, while they kicked up their heels and flashed their knickers, as if they were remembering something that could never be shared by the males in the room. The men joined in the singing of course, but there was something false about their enjoyment of that song, as if they were only pretending to go along with the jollity, some of them vaguely guessing that they were missing something, but not at all sure what it was.

I think the men were secretly scared of the women when they saw them like this, locked together arm in arm and shedding their usual restraint. There was something very frightening about a group of females joining forces, their hair let down, their skirts flying, those strong white legs kicking out. I know it worried me, and I was only a boy of twelve. It was like witnessing the rites of gentle lone bushmen who had come together for a great battle and were dancing themselves to a peak of infallibility. They were giving us an insight to a side of their nature we were not supposed to see. The revealed legs, normally well-hidden, seemed symbolic of the secret woman. I felt we should not be watching it, that the women should have done this dance behind closed doors, away from male eyes.

That night Dix and I sneaked down to the soldiers' decks, further down in the ship. The toilets there consisted of a V-shaped trough running the width of the vessel, through a straight row of cubicles. Water ran continuously along the trough, over which the ranking soldiers did their business.

"Got the matches?" whispered Dix, as we made our way down the gangways.

"I pinched some out of Mum's handbag, while she was doing that silly dance," I said.

"Good. Operation Bum Burn is on its way."

Dix and I had made some paper boats, into which we had placed some cotton wadding soaked in Brasso. We hid in the end cubicle and by leaning down had a view right along the line of the trough. We waited impatiently for the men to come in their numbers, once the dancing up top had ceased and they were ordered to bed. One or two drifted in, but we wanted more than that. The soldiers had been chasing the unaccompanied wives since the voyage had started and some of them had managed to do – we didn't know quite what – with several of them. Dix and I, ever exploring, had surprised one or two couples who thought themselves hidden under the canvas covers of the lifeboats. Guilt had thrown them apart, had them scrabbling with loose clothing, had manifested itself in a stream of whispered foul words from the mouths of the soldiers. Dix didn't like being sworn at. Neither did I. We were in their territory to get our own back, to strike a blow for the absent husbands.

When there was a nice long row of white bums and other paraphernalia suspended over the little stream we lit several fire boats and sent them floating down the trough. After the first scream of pain, we ran. Dix couldn't help himself shouting,

14

"Take that, you libertines!" which was about the strongest language you would get from him. Several other horrifying yells followed and there was the distinct odour of singed hair in the atmosphere, as we scrambled up the steps to our own decks.

We were caught running down the gangways of our own C-deck, and were dragged before the Purser. The mums were found and given a grave ticking-off, told to watch us, and informed that if anything like this incident happened again their husbands would be in serious trouble.

"This may have started out as a joke," said the Purser, "but some of the soldiers have sustained some nasty injuries."

The mums assured the Purser that we would behave ourselves in future and that we would be punished. We were marched back to the cabin we shared with my brothers and two other boys, and informed that our dads would deal with us when we got to Aden.

"You've been nothing but trouble since your dad went away," my mother said. "I'll be glad when I can hand you over to him and then see how many tricks you get up to."

This was a pretty empty threat, since my father had never laid a hand on me. It was my mum that belted us around when we deserved some form of punishment. So I found this statement from her a little lacking in substance.

When the door had closed behind them both women burst out laughing, as if they had had trouble containing themselves in our presence and couldn't hold it in any longer. I heard them snorting as they went along the gangway. I imagined they thought they couldn't be heard, or perhaps they just didn't care?

I awoke one morning, looked out of the porthole, and there it was: a red-brown rocky shoreline. Waking Dix, I then made my way up to the top deck and stared at my new home from the rail.

When the boat took us ashore with our luggage, there were Arab boys in dirty vests and shorts everywhere, their dusty brown skins mocking the pallid complexion of my own body. They

15

flashed grins at me and whispered "Baksheesh?" until an adult chased them away. They tried to sell me fruit, watches, snakeskin wallets. They seemed, even those only five years of age, to have a working knowledge of money that was beyond me. They could add, subtract, multiply or divide any sum you cared to mention, providing it was in East African cents, shillings and pounds.

The land after two weeks at sea felt strange underfoot, wobbly, as if the ground was now floating and the ship was the stable entity. Ahead of me was the town of Steamer Point, the front rank of colonial buildings supported from the rear by an army of flat-roofed whitewashed Arab homes, and behind those, at the base of the volcano, the shanties made of boxwood and rusty biscuit tins with rags over the windows and doorways.

The volcano cone, known as Crater, formed a high brown-rock wall behind the town. It was like a huge broken tooth, the jagged rim of which rose to a pinnacle at one point in its wide circumference. This peak was known as Shamsan, and those who did not climb it were said to be destined to return to Aden at some time in their lives. Inside the cone was another town, named after the volcano. The narrow landward entrance to Crater lay halfway between Steamer Point and Royal Air Force Khormaksar. All around the rim of Crater were crumbling walls and fortifications left by previous conquerors of this arid, humid corner of the south-west Arabian peninsula: the Portuguese, the Turks, others from further back in the past.

Everywhere, in the town, along the roads, in the open country, was dust, sand and rock. The only greenery present was a small lawn in the middle of which sat Queen Victoria on a marble throne, staring out to sea with a look of faint displeasure on her face. There were royal palms running the length of the crescent front, but these trees were so tall their tops were almost in the clouds.

I stood, open-mouthed, amazed at the bustle. Arab longshore-men in longees and roughly-shaped turbans, heaved crates and baskets of fish on or off the dhows, or rather *booms*, while others went out on the bumboats to the liners moored offshore. I stared at our ship, the SS *Dunera*, which looked like a rowing dinghy alongside those giants bearing the P&O motif on their funnels, or even one of the smaller lines whose ships were like sleek racehorses waiting for the off. The port of Aden was truly an energetic thriving place in those days, full of movement and vibrancy. It effervesced every day of the year, even during the hot season.

Dad came out of the mêlée and hugged Mum who burst into tears. Me and my brothers stood awkwardly by in our grey English flannels, looking at this tanned stranger in khaki cuddling our mother. Then he let her go, gave each of us a hair-ruffle, and grabbed the suitcases. We were hustled on to a khaki coach with a khaki driver whose right arm, the one that rested on the window-ledge, had been toasted the colour of mahogany. Then we were driven along the dusty coast road to Khormaksar where a house awaited us.

It was white, flat-roofed and had clean sharp lines. Inside there were floors of terra-cotta tiles sparsely furnished with bamboo chairs, table and settee. It was a honed-down house, having only the essentials. In each of the children's bedrooms, a bed and a chair. In my parents' room, a wardrobe, dressing table, double bed and chair. I loved the space in that house, the lack of clutter, the whitewashed walls, inside and out. Ceiling fans whirred constantly, occasionally batting some rhinoceros beetle like a bullet across the room, when one flew into the blades.

I wandered into the kitchen and found an elderly man cooking a meal. His face was as soft-looking and creased as the skin of cold gravy. Even the whites of his eyes were brown-stained, as if the epidermic pigment had seeped into them like a watercolour wash. He was lean and tall, with a bony, almost hairless head, and looked like one of the Watusi tribesmen out of the film of Rider Haggard's *King Solomon's Mines*. I could imagine him with a spear and animal-hide shield, running across plains of thorn trees.

17

"Hello," he said.

"Hello," I replied, "who're you?"

"Me cook-bearer, Said!" he announced. "Me cook for you."

I was a bit put out. Dad had said nothing to us in his letters about a servant. We weren't the sort of people who knew how to deal with servants, only having come out of serfdom ourselves within a couple of generations. We were a servile people. My farm-labouring grandfather still lived in a cottage tied to the farm he had worked on since the age of thirteen, unable to leave because of poverty and debts incurred by doing nothing more than feeding and clothing his family. The landowner still treated him as if he were a possession, though he was over sixty years of age. When a West Indian once said to me, "My forefathers were slaves of the white man," I replied, "What a coincidence, so were mine." The circumstances were of course different, but the fact remains that my father's generation was the first to escape the clutches of the local gentry.

So what was my grandfather's son doing with a servant in the house? I didn't know what to say to Said at first, but finally blurted something out.

"You're not an Arab," I told him. "How come you've got an Arab name?"

"Me, Somali," said Said. "Come from Africa, over the water. Me Moslem name, but come from big Africa. You fetch him atlas. I show you."

And I did, and he showed me Somaliland as he stirred one of his pots. Later, when I went to find him again, he was on his knees on a rush mat at his genuflections, mumbling and fingering prayer beads. He turned and smiled at me again, but I left quickly thinking I had somehow committed some sort of gross breach of protocol by interrupting him at such a private time.

Perhaps I had.

I felt very uncomfortable with someone in the house who wasn't family. My mother took to having a cook-bearer, who made all

18

the meals and did the housework, as if she was born to it, though she was quite unused to being idle and soon got a job in one of the BOAC offices at the nearby airport. It upset her a great deal that, when my father was not in the house, Said insisted on verifying all her orders with me, the eldest son, for though he obviously knew that Christian women had more power than Moslem wives his pride would not allow him to recognize that he worked for a female. He did not see himself as a house servant, but as someone hired to assist my father in his daily existence, whatever tasks or chores that involved.

Said was a gentle quiet man, illiterate but with an intelligence that had no doubt been quick in his younger years. Shown once how to make a Lancashire hotpot, a favourite in our home, he subsequently surpassed my mother's efforts every time. A Somali's weapon is the knife and Said taught me how to throw a blade so accurately I could pin a cockroach to a door two out of three times. He also possessed a staff as tall as his shoulder, made of African thorn, which I desperately coveted. It was an ancient walking staff, carved with snakes and symbols. There was a polished thumb-fork at the top. I used to pick it up and stroke it when he let me, thinking of all the gulli-gulli magic that was stored in that wonderful stick. In the evenings when his work was done he was happy to sit and tell me stories about his homeland. I often had difficulty in understanding his pidgin, but I enjoyed many of these tales. They were not about lion-hunting, or tribal wars, or anything of that sort. They were about people, mostly his relations. Kitchen stories of how his sister-in-law hated the rest of the family because she was a snob, and how his father had at one time owned several herds of goats and was considered a rich man, and how Said himself used to run errands across the bush country. The closest he ever came to drama was when he told tales about his mother's hot temper and how his father put a spear through his own foot when he was drunk on toddy juice one day. A Somali soap opera that sounded exotic and strange

19

because it took place in a land alien to me, amongst a primitive people.

On Monday my brothers and I started school.

"Class, this is Oliver Carson," I felt a hand on my head, "and this is Jack Dickenson – is *Jack* correct, Dickenson? It's not another version of John, is it?" said Mr Cootley, the headmaster.

Dix replied, "No, it's Jack."

"Fine. So long as we're not masquerading under a *nom de plume*. So many boys dislike their given name."

"No, we're not masquerading, sir."

"Good. Good. Well, I'll leave you to Mrs Gower, your form mistress."

The schoolrooms consisted of a group of huts on the maidan, a sandy patch of ground just inside the gates of RAF Khormaksar. I was dressed in white shorts and shirt, white socks and brown sandals. I felt a bit prissy and my shoulders were painful where they had blistered because I had stayed under a vicious sun too long that weekend. Temperatures in Aden are wickedly high, even during the cool season, and heavy clouds are strangers to the hard blue skies.

We were shown to individual chairs at detached desks in a room of about fifteen children. I was used to benches and forms. Back home in England there had been forty-five kids in my class and I was able to lose myself a little in the multitude. Here I knew all my faults and errors would be completely exposed to authority. I was considered an "idle" boy because I preferred daydreams to lessons, though occasionally I wrote a "composition" (as we called essays in secondary mod) which startled my teachers and worried them for a while.

Looking around me, there were clean-looking kids of both sexes dressed neatly in tropical clothes. A square-jawed boy with sun-blonded hair was glaring at me as if I'd just kicked him in the pants. I glared back. He had a long face and bags under his eyes. Eventually he turned away.

In this class, our form teacher Mrs Gower told us, were children formerly educated at private or public schools, and also children who had attended grammar school. There were only three of us in my class from secondary modern schools. The number of children in Aden was not enough to warrant separate schools. We were to be taught French and Latin, and poetry, as well as algebra and geometry, chemistry and physics. (My brain spun with fear at these words. I looked across at Dix, a grammar-school boy, who seemed totally unperturbed by this horrifying list of academic mysteries.)

Mrs Gower said, "Our first lesson this morning is history. We shall be dealing with the twelfth century. I'm sure you're all familiar with the period, if only in part. So, Julia," she gestured to a girl with strange eyebrows who sat two desks from me, "tell us a little about Henry the Second ... "

The second what? I thought. History lessons were about Romans. I had done Romans until they were coming out of my ears. I knew all about Romans and togas and chariots and Hadrian's Wall. Now I was expected to know something about a Henry. It wouldn't do. It simply wouldn't do at all. I stared out of the window at a passing dromedary pulling a watercart. The camel had a wise expression on its face. I was willing to bet he knew more about Henry Whatsit than me.

Julia was saying, " ... he obtained the throne after wars with his half-brother Pedro the Cruel, and the Black Prince ... "

Dix turned and winked at me and I felt a little better, thinking that maybe the old bag wouldn't pick on me the first morning in school.

I was wrong. The following lesson was English and we did Rupert Brooke's poem "The Soldier". I was asked to read it to the class. I stood up, my face I knew was a furious red. Solos were hated, dreaded things that brought the spotlight to bear on one's inferiority. I stumbled through the verses in my "bible-reading" voice, having to be corrected a couple of times simply because my heart was pounding so violently I could hardly see the words on the page and had to guess once or twice.

" ' . . . some corner of a foreign field that is forever England . . . ' "

Somehow I got through it without fainting.

"Now, Oliver," Mrs Gower said, using the HATED full-length version of my name, "what do you think of the poem?"

I mumbled something like, "S'all right," aware of the many pairs of eyes.

She smiled. "A little too sentimental, perhaps?"

"Yep, that too," I said, grasping at straws.

Suddenly Dix spoke out.

"Load of patriotic twaddle," he said, bluntly.

I waited nervously for lightning to strike him. In my old secondary school such a statement brought down the wrath of heaven, earth and a few other places besides, on the head of the blasphemer. You were supposed to devour and enjoy every crumb of literature fed to you. Teachers considered they were wasting their "precious" time if you didn't. I learned that the only way to get through school life without receiving a dose of the cane once a week was to be as obsequious as possible. In the case where two opinions conflicted, the pupil's was always wrong.

"Please expand on that statement, Jack," said Mrs Gower, still smiling but with a face as sharp as an axe.

"Well," replied Dix, who considered himself Welsh for some reason I could never fathom, "all that rubbish about 'in that rich earth a richer dust congealed' . . . "

"Con*cealed*."

"All right, but still he sounds as if England is some kind of paradise or something."

"A romantic poet might think so."

"Well, I don't. What have you got? A few potty little dales, the Lake District which isn't a patch on Snowdonia, and not much else. He'd have been much better off writing about Wales."

Mrs Gower's smile tightened a little more.

"I might agree with you, Jack, if Rupert Brooke had been Welsh. I suppose if Wales had been the subject of the poem you wouldn't regard it as 'patriotic twaddle?' "

"The Welsh've got a right to be patriotic," stated Dix. "Considerin' history and everything."

And there it ended. She didn't destroy him with fiery breath or have him marched before the Head. I was amazed. If this was an example of education in the colonies, I was all for it. It seemed that the more insolent you became, the better the teachers liked you.

We had a mid-morning break after English. We gathered outside on the maidan where a drinks stall sold lemonade. Dix and I wandered around, talking a bit, eyeing up the other kids. No one yelled out, "Hey, noo kid, cum 'ere," followed by the inevitable fistfight, as I was used to expecting on my first day at a new school. But nobody leapt forward and proffered the hand of friendship either. I went back in to finish the morning's lessons and, incidentally, school for the day since we only attended until one o'clock in that blistering climate, without having spoken to another soul, except for Dix.

That afternoon I met Dix and we went swimming at the airmen's pool on Khormaksar beach. The pool was run down. It had seawater in it and you could swim all right, but the diving boards were missing and there was a general air of neglect about the place. I suppose it was under-used, being a long way from the airmen's billets. To reach it the men had to walk some two miles in the heat. One thing adults in Aden just did not do was walk, if they could avoid it. Kids are different. Kids will happily play snowballs in the sub-zero temperatures of the Arctic or build sandcastles in the Nafud desert under a sun that almost killed T. E. Lawrence. We walked, raced, leapt and did handsprings in the same heat that wilted adults within minutes, and we thought nothing of it.

23

At the pool we saw several of the boys who were in our class at school. In the changing rooms, I went up to the one who had stared at me. He was struggling into his swimming trunks. I was a bit envious when I noticed he had a lot of pubic hair. We were at a time in our lives when such things carried status. I was still very wispy around the nether regions, and consequently whipped on my swimmers as quickly as possible, while gorillas like this kid lingered, talking nonchalantly of adult matters.

"This the only pool around?" I said.

Again that sleepless stare.

Then he said, "Who the hell are you?"

I steeled myself, aware that Dix was on his way outside.

"Name's Cass."

"Thought your name was Ol-iv-er?" he sang in his irritatingly cultured voice. This was the enemy, an officer's kid. He spoke too posh for one of us.

"No, it's Cass," I said through gritted teeth. I started to size him up. He was taller than me, but angular, and he stooped slightly. I knew I was quick with my fists and he looked like a slow one to me. Then he grinned and held out his hand.

"Call me Bags," he said.

"Bags?"

He pointed to the heavy dark patches of loose skin under his eyes.

"Bags," he confirmed. "What's your pal's name? Got a good build, hasn't he? Sporty?"

"Dix," I replied, shaking the hand briefly. It was very soft skin. "Yeah, Dix is good at most sports. I'm not bad, but he's a killer. He's probably out there now giving them a diving exhibition. I hate him really."

"I can imagine."

Just then two more boys came in, noisily, at the other end of the changing rooms. They were flicking towels at each other's genitals. One of them yelled, "Bags. How about a black eye?"

"How about a thick ear?" Bags replied.

24

The two boys, heavy-set and boisterous, proceeded to swing from the metal rafters of the low ceiling, making noises like monkeys. I felt uncomfortable and Bags said in a quiet voice, "Watch out for the Gophner twins."

"Twins?" They didn't look that much alike.

"Yes. Mick and Mac. They can be a bit aggressive."

I left him then and got changed quickly, joining Dix in the pool. He was in the middle of his usual hundred-length warm-up. Later we went out of the pool on to the vast empty beach, which was black volcanic sand. We didn't swim off that particular beach. There were lots of dangerous fish in its seas. Mainly we had been warned about sharks, but there were also other horrors, like stonefish, stingrays, lionfish and barracudas. Stonefish are grey warty lumps about the size of a man's head. They lay perfectly camouflaged on shallow-water rocks, waiting for us to tread on their deadly two-minutes-to-live dorsal spines. The stingrays on the other hand hid under the sand, just off the beach, their tails carrying poisonous barbs at the base. The lionfish had spines like the stonefish, only these were colourful creatures, which invited play. Then there were the barracudas, silver torpedoes which would attack like piranhas and tear you to pieces.

These were not gentle waters, they hid an alien world full of death-dealers. Even a harmless-looking shellfish, like the geography cone, had a sting which could kill. There were jellyfish with tentacles that could stun a man to paralysis so that he drowned. Moray eels with jaws strong enough to crack a thighbone. There were deadly-poisonous sea snakes without number, further out to sea, and in deeper waters still the giants of the ocean like whale sharks.

Unless you were feeling quite suicidal, you didn't play in the shallows of the Indian Ocean. Instead, we collected razor-shells and other beach bounty, to take home to our mothers, the way we would have gathered bluebells back in that far-off land already dimming in our memories. We liked to shock our mums occasionally, by being thoughtful and bringing them gifts. It made us feel

25

good. And anyway, it threw them off-balance. One day we would be scraping Swan Vesta matchheads, mixing the sulphur with some iron filings, making a bomb which would blow the coalhouse door to boxwood; the next we would be bringing home gifts of field or wood mushrooms, or bags of sloes, or wildflowers.

It kept them guessing: demon or angel?

Over the next few days I began to ingratiate myself with my new environment. I loved my stark white-walled bedroom, with its red-tiled floor and curtainless window. It was full of live creatures. The whole house was. Red ants lived downstairs and black ants upstairs: they would have great battles on the stairway, where the boundaries of their territories were indistinct. Both the red and the black armies were ferocious fighters, and took on cockroaches, spiders and lizards without hesitating.

Decorating the walls, the geckos, or chitchats as we called them, kept the insects down. They were pale, translucent creatures with black staring eyes, about three inches long. The geckos shared the houseflies with the spiders. Most of the spiders were smallish, but on occasion a camel spider (big as a hairy sideplate) came into the house and terrified the lot of us, until someone brave enough to get a broom chased it out again. I didn't mind camel spiders and scorpions *outside* the house, where I had room to manoeuvre. Similarly with snakes.

The birdlife consisted mainly of buzzards – kite hawks we called them – that circled the skies endlessly as if they were winding up the world like an antique clock. I used to watch them from my bedroom window, using the thermals to keep themselves effortlessly aloft. They had a ragged beauty, especially in the sunset. Especially around the hooked crag of Jebel Shamsan.

Aden is the result of Caesarian birth during one of those colourful periods of prehistory: an age when surgical instruments were fire and ice. Once the wound had healed it left a projecting scar which was to remain unchanged through millions of years.

A peak of igneous rock, Shamsan had a spirit that reached back beyond my ancestry, past the days of serfdom, further back than the Beaker people, way back beyond the workers in flint, to before a time when humans used their knuckles like feet. It worried me the way an unpredictable wild beast worries me: I was not afraid of it, but there was something almost sentient about that high crag. It seemed to be watching us, and waiting for whatever landscapes wait for – perhaps the passing of transient life?

3

Corporal Oliver Carson walked down the steps from the VC-10 aircraft and on to the sand-strewn asphalt of Khormaksar airport. It was February 1967, and he was in Aden again. The intervening years had been long and full, of military school, of learning, of becoming an airman and being sent to Singapore, then the Maldive Islands . . . of becoming a man. The boyhood years in Aden were remote: they felt as if they belonged to the last century.

He stared around him, at the hard blue skies, the sands, the barren rocks of Crater in the distance. The excitement he should be feeling, after the years of anticipation, had been eaten away by the corrosive acidity of the circumstances of his return. This was the moment he had dreamed of since fourteen years of age: setting foot once again on the hot Arabian sands of his adolescent years. Yet much of his emotion was burning despair – for the wretched state of the colony, for himself and having to come back at such a time, for his lost childhood dreams. There were murder and mayhem on the streets which held the pleasant ghosts of yesteryear.

He could see the house where he had lived, not three hundred yards away. It was surrounded now, as was every military compound, by coils of barbed wire. It made everything seem tighter, closer together, than he remembered it. There were few new buildings, but the open spaces had all but gone.

His feelings were in a gentle turmoil. Ever since he had left Aden behind, as a boy, he had wanted to return. Now he was here, the familiar sights, sounds, smells embraced him, as he had imagined they would. There were the whitewashed flat-roofed houses, looking cool and reserved, clustered around the airport. There was the dry clean smell of the sand, with just the occasional whiff of a desert herb in the air. A pi-dog was yapping somewhere behind an airport building, and familiar kite hawks drew lazy loops over the local dwellings. The new barbed wire had caught a variety of litter on its barbs: Arab newspapers, cigarette packets, paper bags.

His reaction was to run away from all this, climb back on the aircraft and fly off.

For one thing, he was scared. Aden was now known by that traditional British understatement as a "trouble spot": people were meeting violent death on the streets, in the alleys, out on the sands. For another thing, he was now a stranger here: the land might know him but the people did not. The only person he might run into, who would recognize his right to call the place home, was Abdulla. Cass had no idea where Abdulla was at that moment. For all he knew, his friend may have got out of Aden, once the trouble had started. That would have been the wise thing to do. Abdulla had relations in the Hadhramaut – Hadhrami farmers – and no doubt he was now living with them.

Cass peered through the curtains of heat-waves shimmering over the flat sands, towards Khormaksar beach. He could not see the ocean, there were too many buildings along the strand now, but the old swimming pool was still there. He could just see its high surrounding walls. A sadness came over him, as he recalled his last swim there. He kept his mouth tightly closed, afraid he might shout incomprehensibly, like some wino whose mind has been eaten away by alcohol. He was apprehensive, miserable and he was remembering.

A Land-Rover arrived on the peritrack.

"Here we go," said a senior aircraftman standing next to him. "A year in this bloody hole. Jesus!"

"If we're lucky," said Cass, able to speak now that someone had shown him how. He nodded at the armed servicemen all

29

over the place. "Some of us will be staying here more than a year."

Del looked at him, blinking, then said, "Christ, you're a happy soul, ain't you? Well, I'm not going to get shot, nor bombed. I'm going to do my job and keep my head down. I got a wife and kid to go home to."

Cass motioned for him to get up into the back of the khaki Land-Rover. The two of them had come from Nairobi, where they had been training the Kenyan Air Force in telecommunications skills. Now Del and Cass had been posted to a colony, or Protectorate as it was called, at the end of its life. Aden was a place of daily violence. Arab terrorists were killing as many servicemen as they could before the final withdrawal. They were not murdering out of hate, though there was plenty of that around, but because they needed to prove themselves to the Arab population and to each other. In order to maintain credibility, they had to be seen to be driving the British out, rather than letting them leave in peace.

Cass nodded to the lean and wiry Del, a man whose profile could have doubled for Fred Astaire's, and pointed at Khormaksar School as they passed it by.

"Used to go there."

"What, there?" said Del.

They could see a light machine gun post on the flat roof of the building, watching the crossroads towards which they were heading. It all seemed a little unreal to Cass. The last time he had been on that roof Cootley had caned him for it.

A rooftop is no place for people, Carson.

"It is now," said Cass.

"What?"

Del was looking at him curiously.

"Nothing."

"You're going nuts mate, and we've only been here five minutes. Look at the bloody place. Sand and camelshit. Jesus, I dunno how you stood it as a kid. Give me Brixton any time.

30

Hey," Del yelled to the guard of the Land-Rover, whose brown arms cradled a sten gun and whose eyes followed the line of the flat rooftops as they travelled along the Maalla road towards Steamer Point, "what's that thing on the front of the vehicle?" Del was referring to a triangular pole that had been welded to the bonnet and stuck out like a giant rhino horn.

"They stretch cheesewire across the road," said the guard. "It's invisible from a few feet away. If you're in a Land-Rover, or on a motorbike, you can get your head sliced off."

"Who's *they*?" asked Del.

The driver came in now. Though he kept his eyes on the road he spoke over his shoulder.

"Well, you've got the local mob, FLOSY . . . "

"What's that stand for?" asked Del.

"Front for the Liberation of Occupied Yemen – they're mostly Adeni Arabs, with a few Yemenis from upcountry. People say they work for us during the day and kill us at night. Local clerks, and policemen, civil servants . . . put down their pens at five o'clock, go home, take out a grenade or a gun from under the bed, and go out and whack a Brit. Or pay some Arab kid a few shillings to do it for them. Not all the clerks are terrorists, but a few of 'em. The baddies hide behind the others, the ones that don't want anything to do with the killing."

"Don't they get caught?" asked Cass, trying to sort out in his own mind just who were the "baddies".

The driver slowed his vehicle to let an army truck carrying a patrol pass him, his eyes flicking this way and that, as if he was expecting to be "whacked" at any moment. The young guard was looking at the rooftops as they approached buildings, his gaze sweeping the parapets and windows.

"Sometimes," replied the guard, "but not often."

"You said local. There's another lot, isn't there?" asked Cass. "The National Liberation Front?"

"NLF. Yeah," answered the guard. "They're from upcountry. They've got their street terrorists down here, bumping off the

FLOSY people as well as us. The two groups hate each other's guts. The NLF have got a kind of regular army though, in the Hadhramaut, that's taking over the sheikdoms up there. They're communists . . . "

"Marxists," corrected the driver.

"Same thing, ennit?" remarked the guard, belligerently. "Bloody Reds, whichever way you look at it. Anyway, they're all shooting and bombing each other, and whacking us when they can. Bloke got shot through the eye last night, in Tawahi back-streets. Some reporter, not even a serviceman. Then a taff got his face full of shrapnel from a grenade they lobbed at a patrol. Getting bad out here now. You two have come at the right time. They say we won't be out of here until the end of the year . . . "

"Fuckin' marvellous," said Del. "Thanks mate."

"Be my guest," said the guard, wiping his wet palm on the casing of his sten and watching the sweat sizzle like cooking fat on the hot metal. He seemed pleased with the result of his efforts and drew their attention to it.

"Warm," he said. "That's Aden for you."

"When the cheesewire severs a head, do they stick it on a pole outside the entrance to Crater?" asked Cass.

There was silence while both the guard and Del looked at him with distaste in their expressions.

The guard said, "Is that supposed to be a joke?"

Cass was looking at his wristwatch when the army truck in front suddenly slewed violently sideways, skidded at right angles to the road, then crashed on to its side. Dust billowed in clouds from the wreck.

The driver of the Land-Rover rammed his foot on the brake, the vehicle skidded, its tyres shrieking, and managed to halt just before hitting the obscene-looking underside of the truck. Both driver and guard immediately jumped out of the Land-Rover and took cover behind the front end. A second later Cass and Del followed suit.

Soldiers began scrambling out of the back of the crashed truck

32

and took up defensive positions by their vehicle or in nearby doorways. One man was resting his wrist on the stock of his weapon. His hand dangled limply as if the bone was broken, but he still held his rifle at the ready with his good arm. He seemed more interested in what was happening around him than in any pain from his arm.

"What is it?" whispered Del to the driver, who had retrieved a sten from the passenger seat and was frantically searching the windows of nearby flats.

"Dunno. Think his tyres got shot out."

"I didn't hear any shots. Hadn't someone better see if the driver's okay?" asked Cass. "No one's come out of the cab yet."

"Stay where you are," said the guard. "You'll get your knackers shot off, you go out there."

The soldiers began to move around now, running from doorway to doorway, and using the alleys as cover. There was a controlled shouting amongst them. Cass's heart was hammering in his chest and his knees were tapping a tattoo on the hard sand. This was it. He'd been thrown in at the deep end. His first hour back in Aden and he was already involved in an incident.

It seemed they had to lie there for an eternity. The strange thing was, the street life continued its muted hubbub around them. Cass could see brown legs, on the other side of the vehicle, crossing the road. A man went by on a cycle and stared down at them, as if they were playing a game which he found mildly amusing. Arab women were walking around as if nothing unusual was happening. After a while the hot ground began to get comfortable. A low sun burned into Cass's back. The fear left him, slowly, to be replaced by a mild feeling of excitement. Maybe this was all for nothing? Anything could have happened to the truck in front. Brake seizure? Perhaps the driver had had a heart attack? Anything. He drifted away, into thought, and he began to feel drowsy and could have dropped off to sleep. Dust got up his nostrils, made him sniff, which caused Del to grumble.

Then came the shout.

Cass looked up to see a man, an Arab in a longee and scruffy turban, move quickly from a doorway. It was difficult to tell whether he was walking or running. He used a kind of shuffling movement, though not through any disability that was evident. There were other people, other Arabs in the street, but this one had come into public focus for some reason.

The man twisted a little, his arm stiff by his side.

"GRENADE!" yelled an English voice.

Two deafening shots echoed in the street, bouncing from wall to wall, from alley to alley. The turbaned Arab jerked backwards, his arms flying up in floppy arcs, as if they were boneless. Next, he was sprawled on the dust, just beside the road. The driver of the Land-Rover lifted his sten and pointed it at the prone figure. The muzzle of the weapon was shaking.

"Christ!" he whispered.

Cass felt an unpleasant tingling sensation go over his face. Shot. A man had been shot, right in front of his eyes. He looked dead. A dead man. This was worse than he expected. For some reason Cass glanced at his watch. Only four minutes had passed since the first truck had overturned in front of the Land-Rover. *Four minutes?* Surely his watch must have stopped? No, the seconds hand was sweeping round, just as it should do.

"He had a grenade," called a trooper, who was now inspecting the body of the Arab. "I swear it, Sarge. I saw the bloody thing in his hand . . . "

"If he'd have moved, just once, just twitched even, I would have fired." The driver nodded at his sten. His face was covered with sweat and dust and his eyes were bright. The hands that held the weapon were still trembling. Cass could see the man was so scared he hardly knew what he was saying.

"Can we go now?" asked Del. "I don't feel too good."

The guard lifted his face out of the dust.

"Let's get the fuck out of here. I've got days to do. Shit, why me? Let's get the fuck out."

They got back into the Land-Rover and the driver started the engine with some difficulty, before circumnavigating the truck in front. There didn't seem to be anyone in the cab. It was all very confusing.

Once they were past the wrecked vehicle, Cass looked back and could see the soldiers searching the local people, pushing them up against the walls of their own houses, kicking their legs apart. One man seemed exasperated and struggled, but when he tried to walk away in a dignified fashion, a soldier tripped him up, put his foot on the man's backside and pressed him into the hot tar of the roadway. The Arab who had been shot had been turned over, his face to the sun, his arms and legs out straight as if he were lying at attention. No one was paying any attention to him now.

It was a very ugly scene. The troops seemed angry and were probably scared of getting hit by a second attack. Cass could see what must have been the driver of the truck now, stretched out on the ground in front of his cab, in a manner similar to that of the Arab grenadier. He, too, looked broken.

"What a mess," he said, to Del.

Del was pale, and shook his head suddenly, as if trying to rid his mind of the unpleasantness of the incident.

Cass leaned back in the seat, listening to the whine of the wheels on the road. There was a lot of fear around. He could feel it in the air. He could taste it. These streets were once bustling with life. There were people in them, but fewer in number, and they seemed quieter. They appeared to be hurrying from one safe place to another, aware that they were risking their lives out in the open. In the doorways of some military flats stood armed soldiers and airmen. They looked taut and ready to snap in the middle. There were British dead, there were Arab dead. In Silent Valley, the Forces' graveyard, there was a giant invisible mole that continually produced new mounds. Cass wondered if he was going to die here, in the land of his childhood.

He looked up at the peak of Jebel Shamsan, as they passed through its shadow.

35

Why didn't I climb you? Maybe I wouldn't be here if I had?

"Superstitious rubbish," he muttered to himself, earning another concerned look from Del.

They went past a small beach, where Cass had once lain alongside a girl he loved, and he felt an ache growing in his breast. There would be many reminders, of course; he had to expect that. Still, they were good memories. There had been no bitter tearing apart, just an unavoidable separation followed by growing up. The letters had only ceased to move between them in the last few years.

They arrived at the billets: large, long, colonial blockhouses, three storeys high, with many arches and balconies. They were set squarely on a barren slope overlooking the sea. On each level there was only one immense room, which housed approximately sixty beds in four rows. Ceiling fans whirred constantly, moving the warm air around the whitewashed corners. There were no doors: simply archways leading to a long balcony on either side of the room. The back balcony housed the washbasins, showers and toilets. On the front balcony was another row of beds, to take the overflow of personnel, since the billets were overcrowded.

The balcony beds were popular with ex-Boy Scouts, friends of the environment, and lovers of peace. The roof extended over the balcony, but the front and sides were open to the world. During the day there was a magnificent view of sea and at night, always clear, the skies were full of stars. Del and Cass were relieved to find empty spaces out there, away from the hubbub in the room, even though the noise was only a wall's thickness away, behind an arch. From experience in similar accommodation in Kenya, both knew that the lights would rarely go out in the main room: card games, drunken night talkers and record players would continue around the clock, and anyone who complained was looked on as antisocial and put in his place. You were supposed to join in or sleep through it. If you went to bed before one o'clock, you would likely be woken anyway. Bodies would plant themselves on the edge of your bed and a beer would be

36

thrust into your hand with an instruction to get it down you. Any demurring might lead to an argument, perhaps even a fight. Drunks are unable to function without company and insist that the rest of the world enjoy themselves too.

For someone of a sensitive disposition, such a billet could be a nightmare.

A chubby little man lay on top of the bed next to the one chosen by Cass. He was wearing, like most of the men, a towel like a miniskirt. He looked up from a Georgette Heyer Regency novel. There was a whole row of the author's books on his locker top.

"I've only got a hundred and ninety-six days to do," he said, and nodded to his chuff chart on the wall, a calendar with the days done crossed through. "Name's Blue 16," he continued. "They call me that 'cause I always do that sentry duty. There's red, yellow and blue posts with numbers from one to twenty. Blue 16 is the Cold Storage Plant. No one's ever been shot at there. I pay people when I don't get it allocated. They're willing to risk their necks for a fiver. I've always got Blue 16 when I've been on duty."

"How often does it come round? Sentry duty?"

"Depends where you're working."

"768 Signals Unit," said Cass.

"Oh, one of the elite? You an Intelligence bod then?"

"Only communications. How often?"

Blue 16 swung his fat legs off the bed: they didn't reach the floor. He stared at Cass for a moment with baby-blue eyes, before saying, "I'm a cook, work at the cookhouse, naturally. The SU does its own duty. They got a watchtower up on the side of Crater, where the radio shack is. You're all right. You get shot at a bit, but you're high up. They can't sneak up on you and lob a grenade."

"That's a relief," Del said sarcastically over Cass's shoulder, "we won't be blown to bits, just get our heads shot off."

Cass remembered their experience that morning and his

37

stomach turned over. To take his mind off the subject of death, he pointed to the Georgette Heyer novel.

"You like that stuff? I thought it was for women."

Blue 16 nodded vigorously.

"There's not much that helps you escape from this place." He waved the book, keeping his place with his fingers. "You won't find anything further away from sand and bullets than this. You want to borrow one? Small charge, of course. Got to pay for my sentry duties somehow."

"No thanks," said Cass.

"You will," said Blue 16, "if you read at all. I've converted just about everybody on this balcony to Mrs H. Only cost you five bob a book. They'll be here when you change your mind."

He swung his little legs back up on the bed, at the same time reaching over and picking up a fly-swatter from his locker top. There was a swish and a splat which left a bloody mark on the bedsheet next to the podgy man's right leg.

"Got the bugger," he muttered. "Pity it's not a golly."

4

Dix and I soon got into the swing of things. After a couple of weeks I felt as if we had been in Aden for years. A lot of things still worried me, but they were more to do with being a stranger than being in a strange land. It took time to get the measure of possible threats to my well-being: hostile teachers, other kids, authorities of a third kind. Aden itself seemed fine to me. I didn't find the heat oppressive; the scenery was stark it was true, but not bleak. It reminded me a little of pictures I had seen of Provence in France: burning red and yellow ochres.

I learned some Arabic words: *tammam* (good), *mushtammam* (bad), *aiwa* (yes), *la* (no), *mahlish* (never mind), *inta mafish muk* (you have no brains), *taal hinna* (come here), several other words and phrases. I learned to count in Arabic: *wahed, itneen, talata, araba, comsa, sita, saba, tamanya, tissa, ushera* ... and on.

Dix got into the cricket team, and I failed to do so, but that didn't worry me because I was no good at team games. I disliked the idea of having to fulfil the expectations of others. If the team lost (especially a football team) the blame was never ever divided evenly among eleven players. It was usually heaped on people like me, who had difficulty knowing where to be in the (unspecified) formation at any precise point in time. It was as if the others were all linked somehow, by rods and wires, and my link had broken. When one of them moved, the rest of them automatically found their correct positions, while I muddled around wondering whether to be upfield, or down, left wing, or right, in the centre, or simply standing on my head. When there are an infinite number of places to be, and you haven't a clue which is the right one, it's not surprising you end up in the wrong one, is it?

Rugby was even worse than football or cricket. I never managed to get into the social side of rugby: all that jolly farting and belching in the showers, and throwing sweaty underpants at each other.

I was an individualist, tennis player, swimmer, runner, anything on my own. It wasn't that I was not competitive. I was as determined as the next boy to win. I just wanted to do it by myself.

Of a morning, around 6.30, we met on the maidan before going into classes at seven. There was a lot of talk at the time about what was going on "upcountry" in the Radfan, a wild area of hills and desert, south-east of the Yemen. Boys are excited by talk of war and we were no exception. The tribes in that region were undisciplined and inclined to attack strangers. Those boys whose fathers were pilots said their dads carried notes with the promise of money to Bedu who guaranteed safe conduct to the crews of crashed aircraft.

"I saw two bodies brought back from the Yemen," said Bags Williams. "One was a group captain."

Dix said, "You *saw* them? I don't believe you – they wouldn't let you see a dead body." There was a strong note of envy in his voice, an aspect of Dix I never got used to. He was fascinated by mutilation and death, provided it wasn't anyone he knew personally. The pain of strangers did not touch his compassion. He observed such things with great interest, not clinically, but with some sort of heightened feeling.

Bags didn't seem put out at all by Dix's disbelief. Boys at my last school would have bunched their fists and shouted, "You callin' me a LIAR?"

Bags said, "Well, not the actual bodies, true, they were covered by blankets – but I could see the blood seeping through. Anyway, I asked one of the medics afterwards, and he told me it was a group captain and a flight lieutenant, shot down by machine guns up near the border."

Another boy, Alex Rittle, son of an oil-company executive, said, "Yemenis, I bet!"

Yemen, a country the size of England and Scotland put together, was forever harassing the British in Aden. Its absolute ruler was the priest-king Imam Ahmed, who had been in power since 1948 after Imam Yahya had been murdered. He kept people in dungeons, hanging from the walls in fetters, and dropped them in oubliettes and forgot them. Imam Ahmed was a cruel man who kept his country six hundred years behind the rest of the world for his own purposes. Up in the Yemen they carried silver-sheathed curved daggers called *jambias* in their waistbands, which they would use at the drop of a headdress. They were a savage nation at that time and they hated the British just for being there.

I said, "Maybe they weren't. I thought they only had those long desert rifles, not machine guns."

"They got machine guns all right. They pinched 'em from us."

The speaker was one of the Gophner twins. Seeing that they had arrived, Bags said, "Show 'em your photos, Mick." Bags turned towards us. "Mick and Mac have got these photos from the Yemen. They bought them off some Somali, didn't you? Show 'em to Dix and Cass."

Mick looked towards the school, presumably checking for the presence of teachers, or indeed *any* adult. Then he reached for the back pocket of his dirty white shorts and produced a grubby but bulky envelope.

"These was taken when Ahmed pretended to get off the throne, an' his brother took over and started doin' things ole Ahmed din't like much, so he came back an' chopped a few people, see?"

A slightly blurred photograph was shoved under my nose. I stared at it for a moment, trying to make out what it was. It looked like some dead animal, with a skinned tail hanging down,

41

until I realized that it was not a tail at all, but a man's tongue. A chill went through me as I studied the obscenity, a human head stuck on a stake, its tongue lolling long and fat, its eyes ravaged by ants.

"Cor!" said Dix, staring excitedly over my shoulder. "Look at that! Got any more?"

Every culture has its grotesque side. What shocks the adults when they move to another culture, is *unfamiliar* grotesqueness, whereas they take their own for granted, most of the time not even seeing it. As children we were not shocked, we were curious.

There is something about the appearance of a severed human head on a stick that denies lack of life. It seems that at any moment the lips will utter a hoarse cry, demanding that its body be returned to it.

"Who is he?" I said.

Mick snorted. "Who is he? Who the bloody hell knows that, you silly bugger? Some poor geezer who sided with Ahmed's brother. Maybe it *is* Ahmed's brother. There's lots of 'em here," and he shoved some more photos in Dix's hands. We went through them together, studying the swollen, sometimes bearded faces, death printed on their features. In some of the pictures we could see the gates of Sana, the Yemen capital, and it was obvious that these severed heads decorated the entrance to the city.

I took some of the worn photos from Dix and went through them carefully, trying to see if the faces bore a final look of terror on them before the axe had fallen. I was interested in last-moment terror. I used to dream about what it felt like to hang: that last second as the noose whipped tight around the neck with the force of all one's weight. I used to have nightmares about it, wondering if the pop eyes of victims were due to terror or to choking. I was pretty sure it was terror, and the photos confirmed it, because most of the eyes in the heads were bulging.

"Uggh, gungy," said Dix, but he examined each photo in detail. One of them showed a pile of severed hands, heaped on the ground.

"Thiefs," explained Mac. "They lop off their mitts to stop 'em stealin' again."

"They snip yer balls off too," sniggered Mick, "'n dry 'em in the sun like dates."

I felt a tingle go through my genitals at this remark. There is nothing as sensitive on the male anatomy as testicles. The mere mention of violence towards that area sets off tiny warning alarms which electrify it.

We were so engrossed in the photos we hadn't noticed that the girls were sidling towards the classroom. A shadow fell over us and a hand reached out roughly and snatched the pictures. Mick shouted, "Hey!" but his mouth snapped shut when he saw the owner of the hand. It was the headmaster, Mr Cootley, a bald-headed middle-aged little man with a grip like a mechanical shovel when he got you by the back of the neck.

Mr Cootley studied the photographs with almost as much fascination in his expression as I had seen on the faces of the other boys. Then he looked up and said, "Who owns this pornography?"

"S'not porn," said Mac. "No wimmin in 'em."

Mr Cootley gave him a terrible sneer.

"Pornography is not necessarily associated with sex, Gophner. This is the pornography of violence. It is perpetrated by savages and photographed for the benefit of creatures like you, who take an unnatural pleasure in the obscene. Come with me, all of you."

We were marched into his office where a cane was produced. Each one of us received three whacks on each hand. I was used to receiving such punishment, so it didn't bother me, but to everyone's surprise Mac burst into tears afterwards. I think it was the humiliation rather than the pain, but it startled us all, and we let him cry it out in the corner of the classroom. The photos were of course confiscated and there were threats about letters to our parents.

At break-time the girls crowded round us, wanting to know if it had hurt. From their reaction I took it that it had been a long

43

time since someone had been caned at Khormaksar School, which I felt was a good sign. At Felixstowe Secondary School they had caned us for blinking out of time with the music in assembly.

Dix made great show of taking out a small notebook he always carried with him. Wearing a serious expression he began writing in it and continued until one of the girls asked him what he was doing.

"Coot's down here," he replied, tapping the page. "One of these days, when I'm chairman of my own company, he's going to come crawling to me for a job. An' I'm going to give him one – sweepin' out the boiler room."

The girls were very impressed.

"How do you know you'll have your own company?"

"Why give him a job at all?"

"Why not tell him to drop dead?"

Dix put his notebook back into his shirt pocket.

"Oh, I'll own my own company, don't you worry about that," said my muscular assured friend, "but it's no good just sending someone away with a flea in his ear. Always makes me mad when people just go and kill people in films, when they want revenge. That's no good. S'just like switching off the light for them, an' everyone dies one day. What sort of revenge is that? Givin' them what they're goin' to get anyway, only just a bit earlier? What you've got to do is get 'em in your power, control 'em, make 'em pay for abusing you as a child. One day Coot will be sorry he ever raised a stick over me, I can tell you that. I'll make him suffer, an' that's a promise."

One girl however was not interested in Dix's prophecies.

Maddy Swanson, a girl two years older than me who had the reputation of being fast and went out with grown men, took my hand in hers and asked if the red welts were hurting.

"Not much," I said, retrieving my palm. Her fingers were extraordinarily rough, as if she cleaned them with sandpaper instead of soap. I was afraid of Maddy Swanson. She was good at showing contempt for "little boys" like me and I wondered when the snakebite was coming. Maddy was the daughter of a squadron leader and looked like going wrong early, as my mother would have put it. Most of the officers' kids at the school were mavericks of some kind, otherwise they would have been at private or public school, or in a convent, back in Britain.

"There's no need to snatch it back," she said, her dark eyes mocking me. "I wasn't going to use it for anything."

I felt myself going hot with embarrassment as she shook her head, the black curls trembling. There was a little smile around the corners of her mouth and a touch of sadness in her eyes. She was not pretty: her looks were too sensual for her to be thought of as that. I was still waiting for that whiplash strike she was so famous for, but she just said in a quiet voice, "You've got a sweet face – gentle. I think we could be friends. Why can't we be friends?"

I looked around, quickly, in case anyone had heard the "sweet" bit, fearful that I would be taunted for months to come, but everyone else had moved away. Mick and Mac were having one of their quarrels, which always attracted attention because they were so full of rage. Maddy and I were alone.

There was something about Maddy which made my stomach churn with excitement, but I wasn't sure at that time exactly what it was. I knew it was something to do with her being a girl, and sex, but it seemed more than that. In my mind, in my emotions, I sensed a lot of *good* darkness – the kind of darkness associated with warm secrets – and it frightened me. Maddy knew all this, I could see. There was a knowledge in her which was denied me at that stage of my life. In fact it would be many many years, long after maturity, that I caught up with her, understood her as well as any man can understand his alien companions. It's only now I realize what an extraordinary person she was. Maddy was a woman at fourteen, and not just a woman but one capable of great feeling. Had there been some Romeo, some worthy and sensitive youth of her own age willing to talk with her, understand her, love her, she might have been less unhappy. As it was, she

45

sought her Romeo amongst the soldiers and airmen, who roamed her young body like hungry boars, satisfying their appetite for a female in a place with few women, not understanding or caring that this young girl's spirit needed a princely leopard, a lover not a user. They fell in love with her, of course, from time to time, but only as they had been taught to do, with her flesh, not with her soul.

"We can be friends," I said, panicking a little. "I don't mind."

She laid a hand on my arm and said "all right" or something too soft for me to hear. Then I went over to the group to watch the twins shouting at each other. *That*, I understood.

When I walked home over the hot sands after school I found my mother waiting for me on the doorstep.

"Did you change my orders for dinner?" she demanded.

In those days we never used the word "lunch", the evening meal being "tea". I stood there, awkwardly shuffling my feet, while my two brothers, the youngest one grinning, the middle one looking apprehensive, waited for my mother to clout me round the ear.

"Said asked me if we wanted sausages," I lied.

"I told him lamb chops," my mother said, the fury making her shake, "and Said wouldn't say that. He'd ask you if chops was all right, wouldn't he? Didn't he?"

"Yes," I said, hanging my head. She had a broom in her hands and skinny as she was she had a wicked temper which more than compensated for any lack of physical strength. Said was hovering just inside the window, probably hoping for a peaceful end to it all. He didn't like being the cause of disharmony, not the least because it put his job under the spotlight. No doubt my mother had already lashed him with her tongue. I stayed out of range and waited for the outcome.

"Just wait till your father comes home," she stormed, and went inside. I knew I was safe then. Her anger would have disappeared before Dad came in, and even if she mentioned it to him the most he would do would be to put on what he believed to be a terribly stern expression and wag a finger at me. He was no good at corporal punishment, my dad. He was as simple and gentle as a lamb. I often wondered what he was doing in a fighting force, not realizing in those days that any job for a farm labourer's son, which took him away from the land, was a job worth having. The Second World War had lifted him out of his village and shown him that the earth was more than fifteen square miles of arable soil. He had been grateful for that and did not intend going back to pull more rhubarb, weed ditches of thistles or break his back on fields of stubble, as he had done between the age of leaving school at thirteen and going away to war at twenty. As an armoury sergeant he spent his days counting bombs and guns in and out of his lockup, collecting his pay at the end of the week and boozing occasionally with his pals in the mess. That was infinitely more rewarding than humping sheaves and sacks of spuds for a mean ungrateful landowner who used up men like matches.

My little brother Duggy sniggered.

"Gonna get belted," he sang.

"You watch it, squirt," I warned, but he took no notice. He wasn't as scared of me as I would have liked.

The sausages were delicious.

5

Dad went into a kind of mock rage when he was told about the sausages, but that was for Mum's benefit. She was standing by, her arms folded, making sure her man disciplined his son. I fell in with his remonstrations, flinching occasionally as though I thought he were about to hit me, knowing that he would do nothing of the sort. In the end I mumbled, "Sorry, Mum," and her honour was satisfied. A short while later we were all playing Monopoly with great gusto, while Said stood leaning on the doorjamb, clapping his large calloused hands when someone got a double. Our family was like that, from storm to calm in sixty seconds flat.

Dad was a terrible Monopoly player. He was too desperate to win. I think the toy money took on a real quality for him, as he waxed and waned in wealth. He treated us like criminals if we made a mistake, getting worked up at the slightest infringement of the rules, and I honestly think he forgot he was playing with his wife and kids. It was as if he were up against a group of cardsharps, anxious to fleece him of his inherited fortune. He was and always had been a gambling addict, betting mostly on greyhounds when we were in England, but often at three-card brag too. He was absolutely useless as a gambler and hardly ever failed to lose, but he never gave it up. It was something he was prepared to pay for, both with money and peace in his marriage. Mum always gave him hell, when she found he had been betting.

"Calm down, you're not at the dog track," Mum grumbled, as Dad cursed the dice with forbidden language.

"We-ll," he grumbled, "everyone else is raking it in. I'm just not lucky tonight."

"Well, I am!' crowed Duggy, my little brother, shaking the dice like a shaman's magic bones in his little hands.

Dad gave him a withering look which was totally wasted on Duggy. Being the youngest he got withering looks by the hour and would have been lost without them. Duggy got a seven and skipped the old boot over Dad's row of hotels.

"Wheeeeee!"

Dad, his face black as Said's, threw a three next and landed his top hat on Park Lane. Mum had three houses on it and took him to the cleaners. Said went into the kitchen and came back with cocoa, after Dad had had his tantrum.

As always, after a game of Monopoly, Dad talked about getting rich. Most fathers at my new school wanted their sons and daughters to go to university, become doctors or lawyers, or failing that, successful businessmen. None of these things ever crossed Dad's mind. What he wanted for his sons was what he craved for himself: to get rich quick with a tiny amount of effort. Winning the pools was one way. A succession of miraculous wins at the dog track was another. But his real dream was to emulate the man who had invented the cat's eyes used on roads.

"He gets a farthing for every cat's eye they put down," Dad would say with awe in his voice. "A farthing! Just think how many millions of cat's eyes they need, for all the roads, everywhere."

The amount the unnamed inventor received (according to Dad) changed over the years, growing from a farthing in the early fifties, to threepence by the end of the decade, but Dad never lost this vision of finding something to invent, like a cat's eye. Something simple, something that required very little brain power, but something that would be needed in inestimable quantities. His admiration for such an invention equalled that of a layman for Einstein, or a weekend artist for Raphael. The inventor of cat's eyes was Dad's Leonardo da Vinci.

I stayed up late that night, doing an unfamiliar chore. None of

49

the English schools I had been to had ever given us homework to do, and if they had we would have probably regarded it as an imposition and given it the bum's rush. Somehow, in Aden, it seemed part of my new scene, my new self. I even got a kick out of it: having to do it made me feel important. I was like the business employee who takes work home to do in the evening, moaning to his wife that this has got to be done, but secretly pleased that he is needed. Someone was actually interested in what I produced, wrote comments in red in the margin (not always good of course) and gave marks out of ten. At my old school we were lucky if our work had been ticked or crossed through.

The next morning I rose and dressed, leaving the house before my brothers so I wouldn't have to walk with them to school. Dix's house was on the way, so I stopped there and waited for him. He was a dead loss in the mornings and emerged looking as if he had been out drinking with his father until the early hours.

"What do you do all night?" I asked him.

"What do you do?" he replied, indignantly.

"Sleep – but I reckon I look like it. You always look as though you've been fightin' gorillas."

He grimaced. "I know. I always wake up with the sheet twisted round me like it was a rope. How do I know what I do? I lay down with everything nice and peaceful and wake up with the pillows on the floor, my sheet in a sweaty knot and myself the wrong way round in the bed."

"Do you have dreams? I mean are you havin' battles, or what?"

"Nope. Don't dream, not so's I remember. I just go to bed and sleep."

"One of life's strange myst'ries."

"Yep."

We ambled along the dusty road to school. All around us were stretches of sand, where nothing grew and no attempt was made to turn them into anything attractive. Khormaksar was simply an

50

extension of the desert which had buildings and roads plonked down on it, as if by a giant hand from the sky. There were no gardens around the houses, no verges to the road, no pavements and very few paths. Where bricks and tarmac stopped, sand began.

Occasionally a red scorpion would try its luck and dash across the road in front of us, but Dix would throw a cricket ball and squash them, nine times out of ten. We didn't know anything about endangered species in those days. Nor had we crystallized any morals regarding wildlife. Red scorpions were not deadly, but they carried a nasty sting and were therefore regarded as legitimate targets. We did not do the same thing to chitchats.

When we got to school there was a new girl in the classroom. She was introduced to us as Heather McNiece, from Kilmarnock in Ayrshire, Scotland. She had long brownish plaits, a bunch of freckles spreading across her nose, and blue-grey eyes. An attractive girl, with an intelligent look about her. Heather's father was a meteorological officer and she was therefore another one of *them* as far as I was concerned. I mentioned the fact to Dix, who called me an inverted snob, but I pointed out (after he'd explained what it was) that some of my best friends were officers' kids.

"Look at Bags," I whispered during Latin, while everyone else was *amo, amas, amat*-ing. "He's all right. I just didn't like the way she stared down her nose at me."

"You'll be lucky. She wasn't looking at you at all."

I wondered what he meant by that remark, but I was very slow on the uptake in those days. Later, I caught Dix staring at the girl and followed his gaze. She was sitting upright, spine like a flagpole, looking straight ahead. She looked neat, demure, hands in lap: a real-life Anne of Green Gables. Scottish educators were obviously keen on posture. Heather McNiece would have been a credit to my mother, or any mother, and you could tell by just a glance that she would be well-mannered and responsive, replying to inane adult questions in her softly spoken Lowland dialect. My own position in the class was to the left and just behind her, so I could study her features without attracting too much attention to myself. Dix was just to my right, elbow on desktop, chin in hand: a pose which might have been mistaken for one of deep thought, should Mrs Gower glance his way.

There came a moment when Heather McNiece turned and stared back at Dix with eyes the colour of a Stornoway sky. Her broad brow wrinkled slightly and a little smile crept around the corners of her lips. Then she was all attention again, her mind on the lesson, as if she had allowed herself only a momentary lapse of concentration.

For the rest of the morning Dix had a very silly look on his face and even Mrs Gower noticed it.

"What *are* you grinning at?" she asked him in an exasperated tone just before the bell.

"Me, Mrs Gower? Nuthin'. I can't help it if I've got a naturally cheerful disposition."

The rest of the class laughed, but I thought there was something very suspicious about his behaviour.

During break there was a game of cricket on the maidan: a coarse game, which meant I could join in. Dix went in to bat first, which meant no one else would get a hit before we were called back into the classroom. The bat itself was an old one with more dents in it than on a caveman's club. Bags was a good bowler, but contrary to normal rules (time and fielders being limited) Dix began whacking his leg-breaks all over the Protectorate. It was a few minutes before I realized that my best friend was showing off, squaring his shoulders before delivery and sweeping through in classic style to send the ball hurtling between gaps in the field.

"Hoy!" I yelled, after running for what would have been a four on a marked pitch. "What are you playin' at?"

Dix looked haughty.

"Beg pardon?"

"Beg nothing," I said. "Stop whacking it so hard. We know

52

you can knock the leather off the ball, but we're just practisin' here. This is playground cricket, not the Oval."

"You want me to stonewall?"

"It would be a good idea," said Bags, "since there's only five of us all told."

Someone came up behind me and said, "Would you like me to field? I know how to do it. My brother Brian taught me."

I turned to face Heather McNiece's blushing but eager countenance. The other girls, standing by the school doors preening themselves, looked on with surprise.

"You – can – field?" I stuttered, not quite master of the situation.

"Sure, why not?" said Dix, quickly. "Here, you bat, Mick," he offered the willow to one of the Gophner twins, "I'll show Heather where to stand."

I could hardly believe my ears. Normally you would have to prise Dix away from a cricket bat with a jemmy and here he was *giving* it to one of the twins. It didn't make sense. In fact Mick was so stupefied, he failed to stretch out his hand and the bat fell to the dust as Dix strode towards Heather and myself. Dix's round glasses were like coins glinting in the sunlight and his broad face below the straight floppy hair was stiff and shining. He looked like a damned robot.

"Wait a minute, wait a minute," yelled Mac. "What the hell's goin' on here? I ain't playing cricket with no girl. Dix, you want to footsie with her, you can, but I ain't playing cricket with her. This is a bloke's game. Go and play rounders or netball with the other skirts . . . "

Dix whirled, wearing a dangerous mask on his face.

"You talking to me?"

"What?" said Mac.

"Calling me names?"

Mac looked disgusted, as well he might.

" 'Course I'm not calling you names, you twit. I'm talking to *her*."

53

At that moment the bell sounded and shattered the threatening atmosphere. We all shambled back into the classroom: all except Heather, who walked with her head held high, looking as if she hadn't caused an incident at all, but had merely observed the *boys* being stupid. I wondered if she realized she had nearly started a war. If Dix had waded into Mac, then Mick would have had a go, probably with the bat, which would have meant me becoming involved on Dix's behalf. The only neutral person would have been Bags, who was like a Swiss mercenary when it came to violence: only available if there was profit in it. Honour alone would not raise Bags's fists. Insults failed to rouse him to action. He would happily walk away from any fight, any cause, and didn't give a monkey's for what anyone thought. Unless he was offered money, when he would do battle, with cold calculated vigour. There was no passion in Bags, which made him all the more deadly and his fists were worth a few African shillings if there was a war on, say with the Maalla Tech boys.

That afternoon I took a break from Dix and went along Khormaksar beach to the rocks at the end of the bay, below the wall of Crater. There I intended to fish for catfish with a hook and line. A rod wasn't necessary. There were about a dozen Arab boys fishing from the point and I joined them. Although I caught one or two catfish, and a small sandshark, the Arab lads were far more successful than me. I got talking to one of them.

We exchanged names and then Abdulla Achmed told me his father was a clerk in the service of the British Government.

"He has job in Steamer Point," said Abdulla.

I studied this lean brown boy with white salt swirls on his skin, where the sea had splashed and dried. He had longish black hair, sleaked back when it was wet, and along with his contemporaries he wore only a loincloth, tucked and knotted around his buttocks like Sabu the elephant boy. Adeni and Yemeni Arabs seldom wore the white shift and traditional headcloth of most Moslems. Instead they preferred skullcaps, shirts, and a gingham kilt known

54

locally as a *futa*. The young boys often wore loincloths or shorts and vests, usually full of holes.

Abdulla's eyes were black as the volcanic sand on the beach, and they lit up strangely when he talked, as if they were somehow connected directly to his vocal cords. As he spoke, his hands weaved patterns in the air between us. He had the slenderest wrists I had ever seen on anyone, ever. When we had chatted for a few minutes he reached out and took my line from me, tutting and shaking his head.

"This hook no good. *Mush tammam*. Here, you take one from me." He cut my line with a penknife and tied a wicked-looking triple hook on the end. Then he showed me how to bait it with hermit crab. The cheese I had been using was all right, he told me, but there was nothing like hermit-crab tails to catch the catfish. I was a little squeamish about tearing a live crustacean apart and told him I preferred to continue with the cheese. He shrugged, then his eyes lit up again as if he had suddenly remembered something. He held out his left hand, indicating that he wanted me to shake it in greeting.

"What's this?" I asked, suspecting a trick.

"Boy Scout's handshake," he said. "I am a Boy Scout. Third Khormaksar Air Scouts. Baden-Powell my hero. He won Battle of Mafeking."

"He didn't *win* it – at least not on his own. He was there all right. That's where he started the Boy Scouts, as messengers during the siege."

"Ah, you Boy Scout too?"

"I was, in England."

Abdulla shook my left hand, vigorously.

"You come to my group. Mr Wilson of the RAF our Skipper. Mr Wilson is sometimes strict but mostly good fun. You will like him. We have a nice uniform – blue beret, nice blue flash with an eagle picture on the shoulder, white and blue neckerchief with leather woggle, sent from Gilwell, England, holy Mecca of all Boy Scouts. Abdulla is doing good knots like sheepshank and

55

bowline, and splicing ropes together. Have you the Second Class badge?"

"Yes," I said, stopping his flow for a second.

"Good. I am having my Second Class too. One day I am getting my First Class. This is my achievement."

"What about Queen's Scout? That's the highest goal."

He shook his head sadly.

"Mrs Windsor is not being my Queen. I must be going for the Bushman's Thong. This is the leather lanyard, worn on the shoulder for outdoor things like cooking and camping."

"I'm going for the Bushman's too," I said. As a boy who lacked academic prowess I felt the lesser-known Bushman's Thong was nearer my grasp than the Queen's Scout Award. You didn't have to get your science badge, or have to pass any bookworm badges at all. The badges required, though the same number, were things like rockclimber's, swimmer's, athlete's, etc. All hearty exercise things. I could manage those all right. Privately I didn't like the sound of "Queen's Scout" anyway. It seemed a bit wet, a bit goody-goody. The "Bushman's Thong" on the other hand smacked of big-game hunting with a spear and shield: a sort of King Solomon's Award for the bravest Zulu warrior.

Abdulla was overjoyed that we were soul mates and insisted that I come along to his group next Friday. I said I would do my best. We spent the rest of the day in each other's company. There is nothing like the excitement of fishing to bind two boys together: the feel of the line jerking in your hand, cutting circles in the water, the flash of silver as you wind in, then the catfish jumping, its "whiskers" bristling, its body arcing, twisting, finally to land at your feet. I gave all my catch to Abdulla, who had friends and family who would eat them. I knew from experience that my own mother would never let my prizes over the threshold of her kitchen, no matter how clean the seawater from whence they had derived. Mothers are like that. The colour representing the wonders of fishing appears to be missing from the prismatic spectrum of their personal emotions. A mother's rainbow consists only of violet, indigo, blue, green, yellow, orange, but no passionate red, though they will happily purchase from a fishmonger that which they have rejected outright from a son.

"Get those messy things out of my house!"

I knew the words well, having heard them many times with reference to newts, frogs, tadpoles, sticklebacks, grasshoppers, worms, grass snakes, and other God's creatures caught during my junior-school years.

The minarets began to ululate, offshore winds carrying the sounds to us from a thousand mosques. The call to prayer. Sunset. A fierce sky flared briefly before dying. The temperature fell a few degrees to 28 degrees Celsius. Humidity remained the same, around the low nineties. It was time to go home.

Before we parted, Abdulla showed me a trick with one of the fish. He held it out in front of him, his hands shimmered, and the fish disappeared. I couldn't think where he had put it, since he still wore only his loincloth. He then made it appear again, from behind his back. It was a trick worthy of the gulli-gulli man.

"Can you show me how you did it?" I pleaded.

"One day," he said, and I had to be satisfied with that, for the night had come swiftly out of the sea in an all-engulfing black wave. I ran home along the beach, past the *sambuq* boats where the real fishermen sat, sorting their nets by the light of hurricane lamps. Above me the stars shone as they never had in Britain. They were thickly clustered wherever you looked, and one of them dropped from a bunch every few minutes. Dix was always talking about the Southern Cross, down in Rhodesia. We once discussed the northern constellations and wondered who had named those in the southern hemisphere, since all those above the equator had Latin names, like Ursa Major. When we looked them up, we were amazed to see that the southern stars had Latin names too.

"Would've thought they would've been African names or somethin', wouldn't you?" said Dix, clearly mystified. "I mean, who'd've thought the Romans sailed all the way down there?

57

They didn't even have a proper navy, not like the Greeks or some of those others. It just goes to show, you can't trust history." He looked up at me. "Maybe we've just discovered somethin' no one thought of before?"

"Really?"

The next week we joined the 3rd Khormaksar Air Scouts. Dix was just as keen as I was on the scouts and said *Scouting for Boys* was the best book he had ever read. Dix didn't like "cigarette-sucking louts" any more than Baden-Powell. The book was virtually his bible, Dix admitted, and said he had been "paddling my own canoe" ever since he could walk (which didn't make a lot of sense to me). Both of us enjoyed the physical activities: the wide games, British bulldog, camping in the wild. We also enjoyed the strong sense of belonging to a "knighthood", where purity of thought, word and deed was regarded as essential to the spirit. Loyalty and honour, too, were necessary ingredients of character. It was not until later in life that I, at least, was to discover that a choice had to be made sometimes. One could not always be loyal and honourable to individuals *and* governments. Sometimes the two opposed each other. What I do know now is that one can expect to receive loyalty from a friend more often than from an organization. Countries, governments, armies, private companies: these are fierce in their demands for loyalty, but rarely, so very rarely, return it.

Abdulla came to meet us at a prearranged spot and took us along to the group, introducing us to the Skipper. Skip was a tall angular man with a hooked nose. He reminded me of a kite hawk. When he spoke to someone smaller than him, he leaned out and over them, in a kind of predatory curve.

After the meeting Dix mentioned his theory to Skip, about the Romans sailing down the coast of West Africa, into the southern hemisphere, and naming the constellations.

"Save it for your thesis," he recommended, "when you go to university," and then he winked at me. "A thesis is a kind of long essay."

58

"What if I don't get to university?" said Dix.

"Oh, you will. One of you will. Two enquiring minds like yours. How could you fail?"

We knew he was teasing us but we felt very pleased with ourselves. Skip was a navigator on the bombers and knew what he was talking about.

Just before he left us, on the way home, Skip told us to look up at the stars again. We did so, staring into the night sky. He let us gaze for a very long time, before saying, "What do you see? What are you *really* looking for . . . ?"

6

"What do you see? What are you *really* looking for?" said Cass.

Blue 16 leaned over the balcony of the blockhouse and stared up at the hard brilliance of stars scattered over the dark heavens. It was three o'clock in the morning. On either side of them, in lines, were the unconscious bodies of the men who shared their billet. Cass could smell the sleep in the warm air. He and Blue 16 had been to the cookhouse for a meal and were now enjoying that brief glow of contentment and relief of having completed yet another sentry duty and come away unscathed. Cass had been up in his watchtower and Blue 16 had been on the roof of the Cold Storage Plant.

Each had spent much more than the stipulated two hours exposed to the enemy, for the minutes had been long, longer than hours themselves, and the hours had been two eternities. When death can come out of the dark at any second, there is no such thing as real time, only personal time, a time which fear and boredom combine to stretch into horrifying lengths. The elasticity of such periods is a constant source of wonder to those who experience them.

"Alien Intelligence? Spaceships?"

"No, Blue, what do you *feel*? What is it we all want to find in random scatterings of things and events? *Think*, man. Think hard. When we stare into chaos, what are we always hoping for?"

Blue 16 looked irritated and shook his head.

"I ain't that clever, Cass. You tell me, you're so clever."

Cass sighed. "Patterns. We all look for patterns, mate. We

want to see some order in the universe, don't we? You look up there and pick out the shapes you know: the Big Dipper, the Seven Sisters, Orion's Belt. Even those clusters we don't know the names of, we still look for a shape. It makes us feel secure, to recognize something in what's really just a jumble."

"Is it a jumble?"

"It looks like it, doesn't it? But I don't want to believe that. Neither do you, mate. Nobody does." Cass gave a short laugh. "I once had a pal at military school who took five random stars and drew six horses, a man with a whip, and a chariot around them, you know, like they do with those straight lines connecting star to star, to make a picture of a constellation or whatever? It was a mass of angles, but it looked authentic enough. He called it 'Ben Hur'."

Blue 16 shook his head.

"What's the point, Cass? I mean, what're you tryin' to tell me?"

Cass leaned over the balcony, staring out towards the Indian Ocean. He could hear the monsoon breakers crashing on Telegraph Beach. The invisible sharks were out there somewhere, tearing something to pieces. If one was an unlucky human in the water, one would be waiting for the strike to come out of the denser darkness of the sea. *Whack*, an arm gone. *Whack, whack*, no legs left.

"I s'pose the point is, we're fooling ourselves. We look in *The Dhow* every week for the figures, those people shot by terrorists, and make a pattern out of them. 'On average,' we say, 'three people a week are killed.' So when we hear that three or four of us have been whacked, we think we're more or less safe for the remaining few days of the week. If nobody's whacked we think we're winning. Either way, any way you look at it, we make ourselves a hope hole.

"The whole bloody world is a mess, Blue, just a mess. The army thinks it's got order and discipline, but it's just a bloody mess like everything else. You get lined up in rows, tallest on the

61

right, shortest on the left, all dressed the same, all moving the same way to the same commands, and they think that's order. Then they send you out, every which way, like crazy white atoms to get zapped by some crazy brown atoms who think that by eliminating a few of the whites they'll get some order into their own lives. All those millions and millions of people who've died violently since the world began – it hasn't brought us one iota nearer to any sense of order. There aren't any patterns, Blue – we just make 'em up, so we can feel safer . . . I mean, what the fuck are we doing here, Blue? Are we going to leave order behind us? If we all went home today, would it make any difference to things? What you've got to picture is someone a thousand years' time from now, looking back and saying, 'It's a good job Cass and Blue were guarding Aden in the old days. Pity they got shot to bits, but the world wouldn't be in such good order now if it wasn't for them.' You think that's going to happen, Blue?"

"You're bloody bonkers, mate," said Blue 16. "I mean, you've got to look at the big picture. If we go home the Federal Government will get taken over by the communists . . . "

"And you believe that will make a difference to the world? If we stay here until the Federal Government is safely installed, the earth will be more stable, life will be improved for that man a thousand years from now? Crap, Blue. Utter crap. If Napoleon had beaten Wellington, you think we would have been slaves of the French today? That our country would be in ruins? All those men died for nothing, Blue. They were led to the slaughter by arrogant aristocrats who wanted to play soldier. Then the veterans, the maimed and wounded, were thrown into jail for begging in the streets of London. It's all a big con, Blue."

"God, you're a bitter bastard, ain't you?"

"No, I don't feel bitter. I just want to see straight."

Blue 16 shook his head as if to clear it of something.

"Look," he said, "I've gotta think I'm doing some good here. Otherwise . . . "

"Otherwise, you're being set up, sacrificed for nothing, right?

Even if you don't get whacked, it's a whole year out of your life, a year in which your kids are growing up, a year for your wife to meet someone else and run off with him – and all for nothing. The only thing you'll get out of this year is an expertise in Georgette Heyer's Regency novels."

"Shut up, Cass," said his companion, fiercely. "Sometimes you piss me off."

"Sometimes I piss myself off."

They took out some cans of beer from under Cass's bed and sat drinking until the dawn. Then they picked up a pair of binoculars each and crouched down, using the parapet to keep them steady. They watched the windows of the female military police barracks, down below them: a set of two long wooden huts housing the sturdy women whose job it was to search locals of their own sex. In a hothouse like Aden there is little need for night clothing. In fact it is a hindrance. Cass and Blue 16 were duly rewarded for their infinite patience, guiding each other to the best windows as the Joan Hunter Dunns of the Middle East rose from sleep and stumbled to the shower block, their breasts bouncing on muscled chests, their strong meaty thighs (usually hidden unless the woman was particularly tall) banging against each other. Occasionally a dark triangle of hair flashed past the glasses, causing both men to groan.

"Oh God, do you think they'd go out with us, if we went down and asked them?" said Cass.

"I'm a married man, mate," replied Blue 16.

Cass looked up. "Then put down those glasses, you disgusting fellow," he cried in mock accents.

"Not on your life, pal. I don't want to forget what a woman looks like without her clothes on. I've got a bad memory. Jesus, look at her! Forty, I bet."

"She's not more than twenty-three, you fool."

"Her bust, not her age. Anyway, we wouldn't stand a chance. Those birds only go out with marine commandos."

"I'm not surprised. You'd need a lot of tough training to

63

handle one of those wenches. See that one? She'd wrap those muscled thighs around you and break your back before you could say *uuuuaaarrrgggghhhh*. Only a marine, hard as rock and twice as thick, would be able to stand the pressure. Mark my words, fellow, she would crush your bones to make her bread."

"Breasts the size of melons," sighed Blue 16.

"Don't be silly, man, melons don't have breasts."

At that moment one of the other figures rose from the line of balcony beds and came padding over to the two voyeurs. He was a heavily-built, balding man with an enormous stomach and the burdensome name of Rollucks. Wheezing disapproval he told Cass he was a pervert.

"I would be," said Cass, not taking his eyes from the binoculars, "if those were men down there. In fact they're strapping young ladies of my own age – any one of those bodies could double for Diana the Huntress. That's not perversion mate, it's *art*."

"Listen, Carson," said Rollucks, "that could be some bloke's daughter down there."

"I sincerely hope it is, otherwise we've got a female Messiah on our hands. They won't let us live it down, you know, if that happens. You can forget the idea of male superiority and protectiveness. They won't want you defending their honour then."

"Clever bastard, aren't you, Carson?"

"Yep. Cleverer than some."

Rollucks had one more try.

"I mean, that could be *your* sister you're lookin' at – or mine even."

"The first idea smacks of incest. I'm surprised at you, Rollucks, having such distasteful thoughts. Anyway, I haven't got a sister. As for the second consideration, that she might be *your* sister? Well, I'm giving that serious thought. Would I like to study your sibling's bottom, or her fanny? The trouble is, if she looks like you . . . "

Rollucks stepped closer, his fingers like bunched sausages. "Careful . . . " he growled.

Cass at last took his eyes from the binoculars.

"Have you got a sister?" he asked.

Rollucks said, "No."

"Well, it's purely academic then, isn't it? Now Blue 16 here . . . " Blue 16 still had his glasses trained on the solid-looking bodies below. "Now Blue *has* got a sister, and is therefore better placed to complain about people watching her frolic around in the nude than anybody. Blue," cried Cass, "you care if I look at your sister in the shower?"

"No," cried Blue 16, "leave me alone. I'm concentrating."

"There you are, Rollucks, the man with the sister doesn't care, so why should you?"

"I still say it's perverted. They don't even know you're watchin' them."

"You mean, I should go down there, get acquainted, tell them what I get up to, then it would be all right? Listen, Rollucks, you may not believe this but most of those women couldn't care less who watches them, so long as they *don't* know about it. Those that would care don't know either, so everyone's happy, aren't they?"

"Clever bastard, Carson. I'll 'ave you one of these days, you little ponce."

"I'm sure you intend to," said Cass, opening another can of beer, "and when you do, I'll get Blue's sister on to you. She's a brickie, isn't she, Blue? Got muscles like rocks."

Blue hissed, "Don't be silly, rocks haven't got muscles. Now shuddup, there's one that's just come out of the shower. She's drippin' wet, she's towelling . . . oh-Christ-I-wanna-go-home NOW. She's like a bloody goddess . . . "

"What did I tell you," said Cass, shrugging at Rollucks, "not women at all, but Diana and her nymphs, down at the waterhole, bathing away the dust of the hunt."

Rollucks shook his head sadly and went back to his bed.

65

Cass picked up his binoculars again, but quickly became bored with his voyeuristic adventures and began looking at the ships in the harbour, and scanning the waterfront. There were people working on boats and nets, just beyond the Mermaid, and some Arab children were scouring the high-tide line for anything useful. Cass saw one boy of about eight years of age walk past an army patrol that was moving along the waterfront. The soldiers seemed unusually casual in their gait, ambling along with their rifles hanging negligently from crooked arms. They were probably exhausted after a long dawn patrol. Twilight has a tiring effect on the eyes and is a stressful time for patrols. The light is such that movement and shadow seem to become confused with one another, producing many false alarms and a great deal of tension.

One of the soldiers turned and spoke to the boy, who seemed to smile warily. Then the men moved on, wearily, away from the waterfront area and towards the buildings along the nearby roadway.

Cass remained with the boy, who kept ducking down to sort amongst the debris on the shoreline. Then the boy obviously saw something further inland, because he ran about twenty yards, to a dirt pathway. Peering through the binoculars, Cass could see a shiny cylindrical object lying on the path. It appeared to be a battery torch of some kind. He saw the boy pick it up; its glass end flashed in the sunlight as the child turned it over in his hands, inspecting it. Suddenly, there was another kind of flash and a puff of smoke. A second later the distance-softened sound of an explosion hit Cass's ears.

Cass jerked backwards, a little confused, and looked around him.

"Did you see that?" he said.

No one else paid any attention to the remark or seemed to have heard the noise. Blue 16 was still studying the women, through his own binoculars. Rollucks had gone back to reading something.

Cass looked again. The boy was holding his wrist, his face

66

suffused with pain and surprise. There was nothing on the end of his arm except a red stump, which spat squirts of fluid in shallow arcs.

One of the patrol ran back to the boy, called for his mates. The soldiers were alert now, taking up defensive positions, while the first man was wrapping a sweat towel around the wound to stop the arm artery from spurting. There were faint screams now, coming across the maidan from the boy.

Cass's heart was pounding and his mouth was so dry it was like sandpaper. A booby trap. A torch fashioned into a bomb so that when it was switched on it blew off the finder's hand. Perhaps the man who planted it expected one of the patrol to find it? Instead, a child was now without a hand.

He let the binoculars fall to his chest, held by their strap.

"Did you see that, Blue?"

Blue 16 looked up at him.

"What? Where?" he asked, the hope in his voice revealing that the little man's mind was trapped in another set of thought-patterns completely.

Cass stared at him, a little angry, then said, "Nothing. Do you want a beer?"

"Sure," replied Blue 16, "why not?"

Later, when they were sufficiently drunk, they went into the town of Steamer Point, past the Seamen's Mission which had been bombed three days earlier. Past the Convent of the Sacred Heart, which had been bombed two weeks previously. Past the Red Sea Hotel which had been bombed a month before that. When they reached the Crescent they walked along the row of shops wishing they had eyes everywhere. They were not allowed to carry arms while off duty. Each round of ammunition had to be counted in and out before and after sentry duty. They had to rely on vigilance.

"What are we supposed to do," said Cass, "if a terrorist whips

67

out a gun? Stare him in the eyes? Will he honestly quiver, drop his weapon, and run away?"

"Of course he will," said Blue 16. "We're British, man. These spineless gollies are terrified of us when we stand our ground and brace them."

"Yeah, we wish," said Cass.

There were deformed beggars by the roadside who held out their hands as the men passed by. One couldn't provide for all of them. Cass had his favourite, an old woman without legs and pits for eyes. He dropped something in her hands as he passed. Perhaps he gave to her particularly because she was blind? So that she could not identify him as the source. So that there would be no expectations of him. He would be going away, one day, and then perhaps she would starve. He didn't want to think she would be watching specifically for him, his face a picture imprinted on her brain as she went into a gradual decline towards death.

The two men met Del in the Anchor Bar at the end of the Crescent. Del was reading the latest edition of *The Dhow*, Aden's English-language newspaper. Cass looked over his shoulder at the headlines. There was a picture on the front, of a European, his neck torn open and his head at an odd angle. The words above the photo said: SCHOOLTEACHER SLAIN. Cass's blood chilled when he read the name of the latest terrorist victim: *Cootley*.

Cass snatched the newspaper and Del cried, "Hey . . . " but fell to silence when he looked into Cass's features.

Cass read the story. It said that a Mr Albert Cootley, head-master of Khormaksar School, had been shopping in the *suq* for vegetables, when an unknown assassin came up behind him, put a revolver within an inch of his neck, and pulled the trigger. The bullet shattered the schoolmaster's spine, not killing him instantly. Cass realized that Coot must have died in great pain, in the back of a major's car as the vehicle tried to force its way through the crowds in the *suq*. The newspaper photographers from a civilized

68

society, superior in Coot's eyes to the barbarians of the Yemen, had taken obscene pictures of his bloodied head, lolling over the edge of the rear seat of the major's car. At that point in his existence Cass was sure that Cootley would have been only too willing to have exchanged his death for ten years' sweeping out the boiler room of Dix's factory.

Cass's hands trembled as he read. *Cootley?* Still in Aden? Well, of course it was possible. The years between school and manhood are long for a youth, but in fact short for a middle-aged man. There was little doubt it was the same man. Poor old bastard, thought Cass. Cootley would never leave Aden now.

"Wassamatter?" said Del at last.

"My old headmaster," replied Cass, handing him back the paper.

"What? The one what got shot yesterday?" cried Blue 16.

"Yeah, poor old sod. I used to hate his guts at one time – now look at him. Dead as a doornail."

"Good for you, though, mate," said Blue 16 in a much quieter tone.

"How's that?" asked Cass.

"Well, the more people you know who die, the less likely you are to get it yourself. I mean, the odds and all that. It's not likely, is it, that everyone who gets killed knows each other? Silent Valley is full of people who're strangers to each other."

Del sneered. "And that's your theory, is it?"

"Yes it is," said Blue 16.

"Right," said Del, "so if I knock your head off with this, it'll improve my chances of getting home safe, will it?" He gripped the neck of an empty beer bottle and held it like a club. Blue 16 backed away from him a little.

"No. It don't work like that. You got to be a terrorist for it to work."

Del turned to Cass.

"Let's drag him down the backstreets, use him as a shield? Some golly is bound to come out of one of the alleys and do him. Waddya say, Cass? It'll improve our chances of getting home."

Del enjoyed teasing Blue 16, the way some people will tease a dog or a cat.

The three friends remained in the bar until lunchtime, then went back to the billet to get their swimming costumes and towels. The intention was to swim from Telegraph Beach, but the waves were too high. They towered over anyone venturing near them and came down with tremendous force, to drag sand and shingle, and large clattering stones, back with them like mechanical claws raking a trench. When Cass had been younger, Heather's parents had taken him to the officers' club, which had a swimming pool, but the club officials had objected on finding out that Cass was the son of a sergeant and the visits had had to stop. He suggested they walk round past Ras Tarshyne, to Conquest Bay, but Del and Blue 16 were wary.

"It's lonely out there," said Del. "We could get hit from any direction."

Just as he finished speaking there was an explosion some two hundred yards away. Sand fountained upwards as if a subsurface spring had burst forth into the sunlight. The air was full of the hot songs of shattered metal. Then came another blast, and another, within fractions of a second of each other. The tall sprays of grit and dust were quite pretty: golden rain fireworks on Guy Fawkes Night.

It was a moment before Cass realized that mortar bombs were landing around the cookhouse and joined the other two who were trying to bury themselves in the sand. He lay as flat against the earth as he could, knowing that the explosions would send the shrapnel in a low arc above the ground. The idea was to stay under that arc. With each bomb landing, the ground vibrated frighteningly. One mortar hit with a terrifying *thumpcrumff* quite close to them. The earth's crust seesawed and catapulted Cass off the ground an inch or two. His face banged down hard again, making his eyes water with the pain. It felt like someone had punched him on the nose. Small stones and sand rained down, stinging his bare arms and legs. A largish pebble clipped the side of his head, causing him to yell sharply.

There were about seven explosions in all, then everything went quiet, still as it had been before the attack. Cass climbed shakily to his feet; the other two followed. All three were cautious, expecting that at any moment a second batch of mortars would land. They stared around them, at the shallow potholes caused by the bombs. Here and there were smoking patches where the metal bomb-casing was in larger pieces.

There seemed to be little damage. Cass knew that mortars were antipersonnel bombs, like grenades: they showered the area with shrapnel, but even if they actually hit a building, did little destructive damage. Since no one had been standing immediately outside the cookhouse, the obvious target of the attack, it appeared that there were no casualties.

It was with some surprise then that the three friends witnessed a man being led screaming from within the cookhouse, his hands over his eyes. The victim was bundled into a vehicle and driven away at speed, towards the hospital. He appeared to have been facially wounded.

"How did he get hit *inside* the cookhouse?" Del asked a couple of airmen who had wandered outside to look at the small craters in the sand.

"Didn't get hit," stated one of the men. "Not by the shrapnel. He was standing in the queue for custard. The first bang startled the server as he was ladling it out. That poor bastard got a face full of boiling hot custard."

It struck Cass as humorous at first, that someone should be wounded by hot custard, but he heard later that the man had indeed lost his sight.

"Bloody typical," said Del. "The gollies can't aim right to save their lives, but some poor bugger gets blinded by custard. We're as bad as each other, us and them."

"We're certainly not that different from each other," mused

71

Cass, in the unguarded aftermoment of silence following this observation, which caused his companions to stare at him thoughtfully.

When he removed his shirt, after they had returned to the billet, Cass found the back of it was full of tiny burn holes. On further inspection he found small blisters on his arms and the backs of his knees too, made from fragments of red-hot shrapnel no bigger than pinheads. At the time these had hurt less than the gravel stings, so they had gone unnoticed. During the night they were extremely sore, serving to remind him that death had passed within feet of him that day, and touched him with its fingertips.

7

Dix was waiting on the corner of the cricket pavilion in the twilight. He looked sinister somehow, as if he were lurking in the shadows ready to pounce on someone. I wondered if he had been watching for me to come from the other direction and was going to jump out at me, give me a scare. Then I saw him duck out of my sight. The action was strange because I knew he had seen me. Whoever he was hiding from, I wasn't the victim.

I turned and when I looked behind, Heather McNiece was walking to the officers' quarters gate. She had to pass the cricket pavilion in order to get home. The plot began to assume the consistency of syrup. By the time she reached the spot where I stood, the darkness had begun to settle like fine coal dust. Kite hawks were leaving for their roosts in the crags and chimneys of Jebel Shamsan.

As she came up alongside, I said, "Hello," which she acknowledged. Then I ran ahead of the Scots girl to find Dix leaning up against the white shiplap wall of the pavilion. He looked guilty of something. I wondered briefly if he had been smoking cigarettes or setting light to the cricket pavilion, neither of which was in his nature.

"What're you doing?" I asked.

"Go away," he said coldly.

"What?" I was taken by surprise but fell back on the old schoolboy retort. "Why should I?"

He had no time to remonstrate with me further, for Heather

was just passing us. She glanced in our direction, then tilted her chin a little. Dix ran over to her.

"Heather," his voice was stiff and formal, "did Maddy Swanson say anything to you?"

She stopped and gazed at him with those wide Celtic eyes.

"Yes, she did, Dixy. She said you told her to tell me you like me."

Dix shifted his feet in the dust.

"Well?"

"Well what?" came the soft burr.

"Do *you* like *me* back?"

I could tell Dix was in agony and went to stand by his side. This lass from the northern climes of a temperate zone far back in my past was making my friend feel discomfort. I stared at her with a grim expression and received back a smile so full of warmth it would have melted the heart of a Bedu warrior out to avenge a blood-feud murder.

"Of course I like you. I like you both."

Dix suddenly became aware of me and glared briefly into my face.

"But," he said to her, "Cass doesn't like *you*."

"Yes I do!" I blurted, and was surprised by the loudness of my reply. I was also surprised by the content. Until that moment I had believed myself immune to Heather McNiece, even though my best friend had fallen under some kind of spell. She had been just another girl, like any other, no better, no worse. Yet now I felt strange emotions surging through my breast. I wanted this thirteen-year-old Kilmarnock girl, with her freckles and plaits, to regard me above all others as her closest friend. I wanted her to admire me. I thought wildly of things I might say which would impress her, make her think I was worthy of attention. I said nothing. Nothing at all. I just waited, like Dix, for her to pronounce judgement on the situation.

Dix, who had been grinding his teeth up until now, suddenly went silent on hearing my unexpected reply and when I glanced sideways at him I saw that his mouth had dropped open and I knew the shock of finding a rival in his camp – his best pal, no less – had affected him deeply. I felt like a traitor. He was King Arthur, and I was Lancelot du Lac, blatantly trying to steal Guinevere from under his very nose.

Heather said, "Now what do we do?" in a tone with an underlying note of amusement. She was in control. She would always be in control. It was us, the boys, who would continually find ourselves out of our depth, striving to understand, wanting to be considered in command of each new situation, but never managing to be so.

"You have to choose," said Dix, awkwardly. He took off his glasses and wiped them on his shirt. "You have to choose one of us."

"I choose . . . *both* of you," replied Heather.

"Both of us?" I stammered. There appeared to be something faintly immoral in this statement, even to my unseasoned ears. I didn't know very much about boy–girl relationships, but I knew they didn't usually work in threes.

"Certainly," she said. "I like the two of you. You can both walk me home if you like. Meet my parents. They keep asking to meet the friends I talk to them about." She continued her stroll towards the officers' gate.

"You talk about me?" said Dix, falling in on one side of her.

"About us?" I added, being more generous than Dix. I took the left side of our new girlfriend.

"Of course," she smiled, looking first at Dix and then at me, "I told you, I like you both. I've liked you ever since arriving, since that first day when you both stared at me in class. You did, you know. I must have blushed, you both stared so hard."

It was news to me, but considering the new circumstances, I didn't argue. It would always appear to me that Heather had been born with the intrinsic knowledge of how to handle two boys who remained desperately in love with her, long after we had all parted. She handled us in the best possible way, without

75

hurting anyone, not herself, not either of us. She knew it all, perfectly, as if she had already lived one life and had rehearsed it. Since there were three of us, always together, the situation could never develop into anything too dangerous for teenagers to manage. I have always been glad of this: that it remained a chaste relationship.

Dix accepted the situation more readily than I expected him to. After those initial protests in the form of glares, he made no reference to the fact that I had played him false. I think he believed that all along the pair of us had been going for the same girl without knowing of the other's keenness. So he never called me to answer charges of being a traitor, or untrustworthy friend, or thief, though I was all of these things. However, to be fair to myself, I have to admit to being a spontaneous person, not given to planning. It is not so much that I speak without thinking, but that the thoughts up to that point have been submerged and inaccessible. The truth of the words often surprises even me. Dix was a slow and thoughtful planner and I worked intuitively. If I had not been around when he told Heather of his feelings for her, I might never have discovered my own. They were certainly genuine. I was doing nothing to spite my friend, nor was I trying to spike his interest for her. I liked Heather a lot, and was to come to like her so much that I would ache for her company many years after we had been taken to separate parts of the globe by our families.

Heather's parents were sitting on the veranda drinking beers when we strolled up to the house. Her younger brother, Brian, was reading a comic. Brian glanced up, took in the situation at a glance, raised his eyebrows a fraction, then resumed his reading. Clearly this was a boy for whom the world held nothing which could not be assimilated, evaluated and finally classified within a few minutes.

"Mummy, Daddy," said Heather, "this is Dix and Cass, the school chums I told you about."

76

Chums? I had never been called a *chum* before. It sounded quite posh.

The man stood up. He was short but broad, especially around the shoulders. His hair was dark and he wore a black straggly moustache under a positive-looking nose.

"Hello lads, can I get you a lemonade or something?"

We murmured, almost simultaneously, that a lemonade would be just the thing. Heather's father went into the house. He had a slight list to the left, as if there were something wrong with his leg, or his back. Heather's mother sat in a bamboo chair with her legs curled beneath her. She too was small, with brownish hair and a heart-shaped face. She smiled at us as we stood near the steps, nervously throwing glances at one another. Then she spoke to Heather.

"You're a little late, dear. What have you been doing?"

"Netball practice. The boys stayed to watch."

This was true enough. At Dix's request I had wasted a whole half-Saturday witnessing girls running, stopping dead, lobbing a ball at a ring, running, passing, stopping dead, lobbing the ball . . . I understood none of the rules, though I'd guessed a few before the end of the morning, and consequently became very bored. I had left Dix to it about four o'clock and went to see what was on at the Astra, our open-air cinema. Obviously Dix had not been that enthralled with the game itself, only with one of the players, and his plan had been to confront that player on his own at the end of the day. *Hard cheese, Dix, your best friend stuck his oar in too.*

"Well, you know I like you to be home before dark," said her mother.

"Yes, I'm sorry, Mummy."

Heather's father came back out bearing a tray of drinks. Two tumblers of beer, four lemonades. I had expected the cook-bearer to bring them to us, but obviously they did things for themselves in this house. I liked that.

"Here we are, folks," said Mr McNiece, "succour. You lads want chairs, or will you sit on the steps?"

"Sit on the steps," we murmured together, and then glared at one another for sounding like a choir chanting a litany.

"Well, help yourselves."

We took a drink each and sat. Heather went and found herself a chair from the living-room behind her. Brian got up, took a lemonade and said, "Thanks Dad," before returning to a corner with his obviously enthralling comic. There were several moths and flies batting the veranda light, trying to break their way into the white globe to get at the source of the brilliance. Chitchats in the house were calling to one another in a *tik-tik-tik-tik-tik* sound. The evening was, as usual, warm and humid. Jebel Shamsan had disappeared into the darkness but we could see the lights of the boats in the distant harbour.

"So," said Heather's father, "you two lads are from over near the airport?"

We nodded. I thought how nice it was of him not to call it "the airmen's married quarters" and replied, "Yes, my father's a sergeant – Dix's dad's a flight sergeant."

"Good men and true, I've no doubt," said Mr McNiece, "but what of yourselves?"

Brian looked up.

"Dix plays cricket for the school," he said, "I've seen him. He's pretty good."

"A cricketer, eh? I used to play myself, until I injured my back. Did a bit of fell running too. Either of you run?"

"I do," I said quickly, earning a frown from Dix. It was true, though I had not yet had the opportunity in Aden. Athletics were not generally considered to be advisable in 90 degrees Fahrenheit. "I'm a short-distance runner," I added.

"Sixty-yard dash, is it?" Mr McNiece said with a smile, but I was too nervous to recognize it as humour.

"No, hundred and two hundred."

Mrs McNiece laughed pleasantly and said, "He's teasing you,

78

Cass. He knows full well the distances. But, you know, you have to practise anything to be good at it. Do you practise your running?"

"I used to, at home, but I haven't here, not yet."

Heather said, "They're both good swimmers too. I've seen them. They're like torpedos in the water."

"Dix's better than me," I said.

"And very noble of you to say so," said Heather's father. "Well boys," he took a sip of his beer, "do you think you'd better be getting home?"

We shot upright as if spring-loaded.

"Thank you for the lemonade, sir," said Dix.

Sir?

"Yes, sir, thank you, sir," I added.

"You're welcome any time," said Mr McNiece. "Visit when you like, so long as it's not between two and four in the afternoon, when we take our siesta. I've a feeling we're going to see a lot of you and that we're all going to be good friends." His eyes sparkled. Right at that moment I thought he was just about the best adult I had ever met, outside my own home.

We said our goodnights to everyone and Heather walked us to the compound gate, where we said goodnight to her again.

"Your parents are nice," said Dix, getting in before me.

"Yeah, great," I added. "I really like your dad – and your mum."

"I knew you would," she said. "Well, we're all good chums now. I think you're super, both of you. Goodnight boys."

"Goodnight, Heather," we chorused for the third time.

My heart was full to bursting that evening, as we walked home under the stars. *Super*. She had said we were super. I *felt* super, though it wasn't a word I'd used before. To add to our happiness Dix found a skink in the sand, under one of the periphery lights. We thought it was a snake at first, when a small running hump appeared near our feet, raising a long scar on the smooth desert dust. Dix grabbed it though and it turned out to be a lizard that burrows just below the surface. He took it home, promising we should both get a good look at it in the morning before church, the next day being Sunday.

When I got indoors they'd had their tea and I was told if I wanted anything to go and boil myself an egg. Said was in the kitchen and he smiled his brown-toothed smile at me. He was polishing his staff. I stared at the stick thoughtfully. It was surely a magic rod. Perhaps it was the very same that Moses used to part the waters of the Red Sea?

"You like me stick?" laughed Said, his bald head gleaming under the kitchen light.

I nodded.

"Him nice stick, eh? Said's fighting stick." He continued to polish it vigorously, while I boiled my egg.

When I went back into the living room my mother was sitting under the fan trying to keep cool. Dad had gone down to the sergeants' mess for a drink. Although she was small and lean Mum felt the heat badly. I ate my egg in silence and then said I was going to bed.

"So early?" she said.

"Yep. Church tomorrow." My parents didn't go to church. I don't think they believed or disbelieved, they just didn't think about it too much.

"Mother," I said, making her look at me sharply, since I only called her that when I was about to say something serious, like *"I've just blown the coalhouse to bits with a home-made bomb . . ."*

"What is it, dear?" she asked, apprehensively, leaning forward in her chair.

"Mother, I've got a girlfriend."

She leaned back, a look of relief on her face.

"That's nice."

"I like her a lot."

"Well I'm sure you do, dear, but people don't get *feelings* for one another until they're much older than you. Not strong feelings."

"She's just a friend – like Dix."

"That's what I thought."

Dad walked in through the doorway, slightly tipsy.

"What's this?" he said.

Mum replied, "He's got a little girlfriend."

"Oh." Any interest had evaporated.

The next day I dressed in my whites including socks, put on my best sandals, slicked my hair back, and went to collect Dix for church. He was similarly attired. The skink had escaped during the night, so we ambled to church slowly. There was an old beggar on a rattan bed just outside the gates of the camp and we stopped to chat to him as usual. He had told us he had been there since the beginning of time and we half believed him. His yellowish body looked dried and withered, like a roll of parchment. He always offered us a drink from his water-bottle which was wrapped in wet rags to keep the contents cool, but we were squeamish and always refused. It didn't seem to bother him, because he laughed at us from a toothless cavern of a mouth. I wondered what it was like to own nothing but a bed and a water-bottle as the old man did. It seemed a good thing in one way: a bit like Christ or Gandhi. Then again, when I thought of myself in the same position, I began adding things to the list: a bed, a water-bottle and my comics; a bed, a water-bottle, my comics and a knife for cutting bread and meat; a bed, a water-bottle, my comics, a knife, and a sheet for keeping off the mosquitoes, and so on, until the possessions mounted to the point where I would need a house to keep them all in.

Inside the wooden church it was cool. The padre was a Welshman named Griffith, a big man with a big voice, who breathed fire and chewed brimstone. Not so long ago the Reverend Griffith, instead of standing in his pulpit to deliver his sermon, used to pace backwards and forwards across the church in front of the altar, employing a clenched-fist salute when it came to making an emphatic statement about the Lord, and stamping his size-ten sandal when it came to putting down Satan. One Sunday three weeks earlier the scout groups had had a church parade. Skip decided to play a joke on the padre and spoke to us beforehand.

"When the padre moves to the left-hand side of the church I want you all to smile and look interested," said Skip, "but when he marches over to the right side, drop the smiles and look bored and listless. Got it?"

We all went along with the joke and the poor Reverend spent the last half of his sermon on the extreme left side of the church, hunched against the pulpit, perhaps only subconsciously aware that he had a tremendous grip on his congregation from that position.

From that day forth the padre had given his sermons from the pulpit, having been psychologically herded there by our scoutmaster. I believe the Reverend Griffith would have destroyed Skip with his breath if he ever found out what had been done to him. I trembled at the thought, being one of the sheepdogs.

8

I used to lie awake at nights thinking of the ghosts that roamed Shamsan's forbidding peak and wondering whether I would ever have the courage to climb to the summit, to ensure that I would never return to the peninsula. On waking, the room would always be filled with light: hard, brilliant light. I would first hear the muezzins calling the faithful to prayer, then the sound of the dromedaries being woken by the *levies*, the Arab camel soldiers who served the British, in the stables nearby. Finally, there would be the noises created by Said, clattering around with his pots and pans, in the kitchen below.

One morning I went down the stairs to find many bodies scattered over the stone steps and rises. During the night there had been a tremendous battle between the red and black ants. While the rest of the world slept the insects had fought their world war, counting territorial gains and losses in inches. Since there were some live red ants swaggering around near the top of the stairs, I guessed they had managed to better the black ants. I wondered if I would see a complete annihilation of the latter while I was part of the household, or whether these were just tidal advances and retreats that I was witnessing.

I went outside the house to the place where the bathwater flowed from an open-ended pipe. There I was growing some tomatoes from seed in the soapy wastewater. This was my third attempt at producing some real edible fruit: all previous efforts had failed. The tomato plants seemed to shoot upwards in a matter of a few days, faster than bamboo, only to wither on tall thin stems before the fruit came. The only greenery that seemed to flourish with great abandon in my little garden were plants we called "cod-liver oil trees" with broad dark-green fronds the shape of horse-chestnut leaves. These we had to hack down with the breadknife, like rainforest foliage, every few weeks because they got so tall and thick they threatened the light at the kitchen windows. The cod-liver oil trees seemed to suck in detergents and scouring fluids as if they were full of nourishing goodness, essential to plant growth. We watched in amazement and alarm as these plants, which had appeared of their own accord out of the Aden dust, attempted to swallow the house and turn it into something resembling an ancient tribal temple overcome by the Amazon jungles.

Of a Saturday, Dix, Abdulla and I used to like to wander the backstreets of Tawahi. We would walk around the shoreline from Khormaksar to Steamer Point, past the stretch of beach where Arab dhows, or *booms*, were being built. The smell of freshly-cut tawny timber is with me even today as I recall the great ribcages of those seagoing craft, rising out of beds of curled woodshavings and sawdust. So far as I can remember, no metal was used to fashion a dhow, just cleverly-designed joints, and pegs that swelled within their holes. The brown-bodied craftsmen would clamber over the thick beams, tapping, scraping, their only tool a kind of honed adze that in the right hands could shave to the thickness of paper. When the craft was finished, the whole boat was painted inside and out with brooms dipped in vegetable oil, to seal it from the sea.

On the water, under full sail, a dhow revives that exciting sense of Arabesque magic that children feel when reading the *Arabian Nights* and *Sinbad the Sailor*. A dhow moves and creaks over all its length, the sail cracks as it fills with wind, and the sailors work the hemp sheets the way their forefathers have done for thousands of years. I never tired of watching these great wooden whales of the Indian Ocean as they rolled through the surf with

84

ungainly motion, bound for the coast of Africa or one of the islands, such as Zanzibar.

From the open shipyards of ancient craftsmen we would follow the harbour round to where we could see the modern ships, out in the bay, towards Little Aden on the twin peninsula. There were a great many liners in those days, carrying passengers to and from India, Hong Kong and Australasia. Their funnels were painted with their steamship company logos and we used to keep a tally of the ships, the way boys in Britain used to collect the numbers of steam trains. I loved the high-sounding names of the shipping lines: Cunard, Canadian Pacific, Aberdeen and Commonwealth, Union-Castle, Pacific and Orient, Italian. There were other smaller lines such as Libby (or Bibby?) which have almost slipped away from my memory now. I was into ships in a big way in my youth. I had a picture of the White Star Line's *Titanic* on my bedroom wall and further along, directly in its path, a photograph of the actual iceberg that had sunk her, the caption underneath pointing out the paintmarks from *Titanic*'s bows. Someone on one of the rescue ships had taken this picture of the shipwrecker.

One Saturday, about seven months after the date I had first arrived in Aden, the three of us were eating pancake bread straight out of the clay oven, just two streets back from the Crescent. We were sitting on the back of a cart which had been left propped against a wall. Abdulla was playing tricks with strips of bread, making them vanish and then reappear. Dix and I were only half paying attention, we had seen Abdulla do this so many times before. His gulli-gulli magic was more for his own amusement than ours. Just then an Arab in a blue *futa* stopped in his tracks, and came over to us.

"*Salaam aleikum!*" he said.

"*Y'aleikum salaam,*" we replied through mouthfuls of bread.

The "peace be with you" greetings over, the man spoke quietly to Abdulla, who seemed to know the man, and nodded once or twice towards Dix and myself as they conversed.

"What's he saying?" asked Dix through a mouthful of bread.

Abdulla said, "He is my uncle, Hussein. He asks that we go to take tea at the house of my aunt."

"Tea?" It wasn't the most exciting prospect of a day in Tawahi to two English boys looking for adventure. We preferred roaming the waterfront or rooting through the shops with their daggers and bullwhips, smelling the camphorwood chests and feeling the smoothness of sinister jade carvings.

Abdulla shrugged.

"It would be impolite to refuse," he said.

So we jumped down from the cart, saying, "*Aiwa, tammam,*" and followed the uncle through the backstreets to a hovel made out of biscuit tins under the shadow of Shamsan. There was a strip of hessian serving as a door, which was thrown aside and we entered a gloomy interior with a low ceiling. We sat on the dirt floor while Hussein called to Abdulla's aunt somewhere out the back. The man then smiled at us and asked us our names. He spoke in Arabic, some of which we understood, and we replied with some help from Abdulla.

"What's your uncle do?" I asked Abdulla, during a pause in conversation.

"Now? He tries to get a job in Aden. He was Hadhrami goat farmer, out near the Radfan, but the Qotaibi tribesmen kill all his goats one day for eating their grass."

"What grass? They own it?" I asked.

"They say so," answered Abdulla.

"Why didn't he kill *them?*" I asked, aware of how things were settled out in the Hadhramaut desert.

"They were too many. Now he is asking if you can give him job, so he can feed my cousins? Can you give him job, Cass?"

I looked at Abdulla, then at his uncle, helplessly. Me? I didn't have any jobs to give. I knew my mother was thinking of employing a sweep-boy to help Said, but I couldn't see Hussein in this capacity, sweeping sand from the house all day. What was I to do? I wanted to help, but I was just a boy of twelve.

I said all this to Abdulla.

"But your mother," my friend replied, "she is clerk to employ workers from the Adeni, yes? You must ask her, Cass, to give my uncle job?"

He didn't mean I *must* ask her, he meant *would* I ask her. I thought about this and my stomach turned over. How would I go about such a thing? *Mum, I met this Arab who lives in a biscuit tin? Can you find him a job somewhere?* She would go bonkers. Still, I had to try. We had been offered and had accepted hospitality from the gentleman in question and therefore I had to do my best to fulfil his request.

"Can't your dad find him a job, Abdulla? I mean, he's a clerk too," I said.

"My father has not command over jobs, like your mother. He works on the ledgers for pay."

"Oh."

The tea arrived, in old Heinz beans cans, and we drank it down with murmurs and belches to show how delicious it was. Abdulla's aunt, dressed in a black shift with a mask on her face made of cardboard and black insulating tape, fussed around with some flour stuff in the corner while we drank, glancing up every so often to take us in with brown eyes, which was all we could see of her. She reminded me of some dark predatory bird with her beak-like mask, but her eyes were soft and kindly. I smiled at her and the corners of the eyes crinkled in return.

Then I asked Abdulla, who was literate in English, to write down his uncle's name on a piece of paper. Abdulla found the stub of a pencil from somewhere in his *futa* and a cigarette packet was obtained for the paper. I was given the name and age of Hussein. It was now up to me to find him employment.

"I thank you for this thing," the boy whispered, as we left the house of biscuit tins, but I hadn't done anything yet.

Abdulla went off with some other Arab boys to dive for coins from liners that had just hove into harbour. Dix and I walked home along the shoreline, skimming scallop shells into the wind, so that they curved and returned to us like boomerangs. The activity kept us busy and made talking difficult. It was a way we had of letting the silence fall between us, when we wanted time to think.

That evening I put the problem to Heather, as the three of us sat on the veranda of her house, breathing the warm evening airs.

"What am I gonna do?" I groaned. "My mum will go up the wall if I ask her something like this. She hates favouritism of any sort. She calls it *corruption*. If I wanted a job for myself, she'd make me wait in the queue like everyone else. What am I gonna do?"

"We'll have to think of some scheme," said Heather.

Dix suggested, "You could soften her up – with a present? We could all chip in. I've got a bit of pocket money left over."

"Would that work, Cass?" Heather asked, her eyes on me.

"I dunno," I said. "I could buy some of that scent she likes so much – stuff called Evening in Paris in a little blue bottle. I did that when I blew the coalhouse to bits in England."

Heather laughed. "Blew up the coalshed?"

"With a bomb I made out of Swan Vesta matchheads and iron filings. I rammed 'em in a piece of copper pipe and made a fuse out of string and saltpetre . . . "

"Yeah, well this ain't gettin' the problem solved, all this chatter about bombs, is it?" said Dix testily. I could see he was getting jealous over the attention Heather was giving me. There was a delicate balance to maintain in the relationship we had and it meant one often had to sacrifice individual attention for the good of the group. Such limelight was sweet however and it was difficult to let it go.

"I stuck it under the coal and lit the fuse."

"Did it work?" asked Heather, her eyes fixed on mine.

88

"What, the bomb? 'Course it did. It blew the coalhouse door to smithers. There were bits of coal all over the yard."

"No, you dope," snarled Dix, "the gift. This Paris Evenings stuff. Did it work on your mother?"

But Heather had meant my bomb and she smiled at me. When I smiled back she suddenly went very serious again and seemed to move slightly towards me, as if she wanted to hug me, possessively. I was a little shocked that she should be impressed by my wayward past. I was often surprised by girls' reactions to things. When you thought they would be bound to disapprove of something you'd done, they gave you that anxious-fond look, as if you had said you were going away somewhere for good.

However, we never ever touched one another, except by accident, and the moment was shattered by Dix.

"Well, did it work?" he cried.

"No," I said.

"Well, I'm glad we've got to the bottom of *that*," Dix said, and I knew he was aware of losing a little ground with our girlfriend. He really had no need to worry. Tomorrow it would be him overtaking me. We swayed back and forth in Heather's favours, never falling out of them, just gaining a few yards over the other boy occasionally. Like the red and black ants, there was no possibility of an overwhelming victory, only of extending territory for a short time.

We never got any further though. Maddy Swanson suddenly appeared on the steps of the veranda. She looked pale and her hair was a mess, as though she'd thrown on her dress quickly, pulling it over her head without undoing the buttons. She was also barefoot.

"Can I speak to you a minute, Heather?" she said.

"Yes, of course," said Heather, "do you want the boys to leave?"

We all sensed something terrible had happened. Dix and I stood up, ready to go. Our curiosity was not as strong as the

89

desire to escape the knowledge of female problems. Maddy said in a tired-sounding voice, "No, let them stay."

We remained standing and everyone fell silent for a while, then Maddy cried, "I'm pregnant. I've got myself pregnant."

I wanted the ground to swallow me up. My blood rushed to my face and I stood there, burning.

Dix blurted out, "What a stupid thing – you're only fourteen."

To be fair to him, it was pure reaction. The words meant nothing, nothing at all. I'm sure it was just a case of having to say something.

Heather said sharply, "Be quiet, Dixie," then to Maddy, "Was it Bill?"

Maddy's eyes were wet and once she was under the light I could see the red rims around them. Heather took the girl's left hand and Maddy reached out with the other hand and grasped mine, as if she wanted support from both sides. She squeezed my fingers so hard they hurt and I blinked through the pain. Heather and I sat down with the older girl, so there were three of us like the wise monkeys, in a line on the step, clutching each other, while Dix stood by looking spare and awkward. My heart was beating rapidly and I wanted to be anywhere but there at that moment. It seemed to me that Dix and I were out of our depth. We were drowning in the awfulness of this young girl's distress.

"They're sending our family back to England," said Maddy. "My dad's going berserk. He was up for promotion, but they're sending us all back because of me and Bill."

"What about Bill?" asked Heather. "What about Bill, Maddy? Is he going home too?"

Bill was an airman, a young man of eighteen who worked in the clothing stores.

"My dad told him to eff-off," said Maddy. She laughed then, into my face. 'Look at that. I can *do* it, but I can't *say* it. *Fuck*. There, I've said it . . ." She burst into tears and leaned on

Heather's shoulder. I glanced up at Dix whose face was flaming. We both looked away from each other again, quickly.

Suddenly, Maddy looked at me, fiercely.

"Everybody keeps on at me, asking me why I did it. My dad, especially. On and on at me. Why's he think I did it? To spite him? It just happened, that's all. The thing is, you see . . . " her voice was thin and strained, "the thing is, the *trouble* is, I'm *scared*, and nobody seems to ask me that. I'm bloody frightened. I'm frightened . . . "

At this moment Heather's mother had appeared from somewhere in the house and stepped out on to the balcony. Her eyes swept over us and she said quietly, "What's going on out here, Heather?"

Heather said, very calmly, "Maddy's found out she's having a baby. Her father's very angry."

Mrs McNiece stared for a moment at the sobbing girl and then looked at Dix and me.

"You two, off you go. You can come back some other time. Heather, you and Maddy come into the house. Come along," she said in a gentle voice, to Maddy, "come and sit down in a comfortable chair. Off you go, lads."

"Yes, Mrs McNiece."

"You can come swimming with us at the weekend, if you wish," she added over her shoulder, "at Gold Mohur Club."

We ran off into the night, glad to be out of it.

Dix and I didn't talk about it on the way home, so I don't know what he was thinking or feeling. My own thoughts were fairly selfish ones. I was glad I was a boy and that sort of thing couldn't happen to me. Not directly. I could be the cause of such distress, probably, but not the victim.

When I got home I went to see Said and asked him if I could touch his staff for luck. He let me hold the African thorn stick and I felt the magic go into me. I wished for Maddy, and then I wished for a job for Abdulla's uncle. Somehow I was going to get Hussein his job, though I still had no real plan. Maddy's plight had made me more determined, for some reason, that the man whose goats had been slaughtered by the Qotaibi should have work. The two things didn't seem to be connected in any way, but one gave rise to feelings about the other.

As I went up the stairs to bed I saw that the black ants had gained some ground during the day, recapturing three steps and rises. Red losses had no doubt been swept up by Said and thrown in the wastebin, along with those blacks who had been in the front line. What a way to treat heroes. War is hell, even for ants.

9

Cass had been in the watchtower for over an hour. On his right was the rockface which led to the peak of Shamsan. To his rear, further down the hill on which the watchtower was perched, was a single-storeyed longhouse known as the radio shack, within which his colleagues were at work secretly listening to the messages passed between groups of Arabs.

The war in the Yemen was a long way away: messages between royalists loyal to the deposed Imam, and republicans and Egyptian troops, were only of peripheral interest to the intelligence officers who deciphered and translated them.

The NLF however was active in the sheikdoms in the north of the Protectorate, rapidly eroding the aristocratic power of the Federation sheiks. The Marxist NLF were not just a bunch of guerrillas, but had formed into a regular army. They were dedicated to driving the British out of Aden, even though the colonial power was in the process of leaving: local politics demanded that they be shot and killed where possible to provide credibility to their potential successors.

Thus in Aden itself the NLF and FLOSY terrorists were picking off the British residents and soldiers, and each other, one by one. Europeans out shopping were gunned down in the street. Blocks of flats containing service families were the targets of rocket and mortar attacks. Grenades were thrown into clubs and cinemas. Bottle bombs were rolled into bars along the Crescent. There were booby traps all over the landscape, mainly along the Maalla Straight, nicknamed Murder Mile. Arab children had lost hands and feet, picking up items left for British soldiers to find. Adeni and Yemeni Arabs were assassinated in broad daylight.

It was the violence that end of Empire often created. The British were going before the year was out but wanted to leave the Federation sheiks in government. The republicans were having none of it.

Cass was one of those young men caught up in this storm of death and destruction. He had no wish to be there. A few years previously he had been a playmate of those Arabs he was now told were his enemies. There was a growing sense within him that he was betraying his own childhood. He was like a man who was experiencing a bitter end to what was once a happy marriage: all the good years were being soured by the final few venomous weeks.

Directly in front of the watchtower was the edge of the steep slope, almost a cliff, that fell down to Tawahi some two or three hundred feet below. Cass overlooked the backstreets and rooftops of the whole town. He could see the shopping crescent up ahead, and beyond that the maidan that fronted the harbour. Steamer Point was like an aerial map, spread at his feet.

Now, down below him, in the town, there were murmurings and whisperings and secret doings. There were lights down there which never went out, and others which never came on. Somewhere in that shadowy urban world below him there was supposed to be a brothel, a mythical whorehouse called Jasmine's. Everyone claimed to know someone whose friend had found Jasmine's by accident, while out on patrol, or on a house search for terrorists. This friend had of course taken time out to indulge in an oriental orgy which had cost him nothing but a packet of cigarettes. The idea that one would actually enter the backstreets in quest of Jasmine's, even if one knew its location, was of course insane. There were apocryphal tales of the man who had got drunk, gone whoring and found love and death sharing the same bed.

He could see the dark silhouettes of an army patrol cautiously making their way around the backstreets, for the sole purpose of creating a *presence* amongst the locals. The army could not go to the terrorist, who hid amongst civilians, so the terrorist was invited to go to the army. *Come and toss a grenade at us*, the patrol was saying, *so we can get you in the open.* A tick-infested pi-dog crossed their path, slinking from one hovel to another, and had them twitching for a moment.

Cass had come back to a different Aden from his youth. He was forced to watch Arabs he recognized being searched with unnecessary roughness by angry British troops, indignities thrust upon them which he knew would have them weeping in frustration and rage once out of sight of the soldiers, who in turn were losing comrades to the terrorist bombs and bullets. He saw honour being spat on and trodden into the dust. The very air was choked with emotion.

All the men who worked at the radio shack below had to take a turn at sentry duty, guarding the others. Cass was supposed to be watching for any activity in the town below him. If he saw or heard something, a shooting or a grenading, he reported it over the field telephone to the command post located in Steamer Point barracks. Some of these happenings would appear on the local radio network "Incident Report" the following day.

A bolt-action Lee-Enfield Mk4, the design of which had changed very little since the Second World War, was cradled in Cass's arms like a baby. It was a heavy weapon and awkward to carry. He could have rested the muzzle on the parapet of the watchtower, except that the section flight sergeant in charge of discipline had a habit of creeping up on the tower and if he caught anyone "mishandling" their rifle he gave them extra sentry duty. So far the evening had been quiet. Cass had spent the time looking down on Arab households preparing for the night hours. Dogs were barking. Dogs were always barking in some corner of the town. Occasionally a baby wailed, until it was comforted. All sounds drifted up to Cass in his tower above the town. Time passed very slowly.

Suddenly, just when Cass was lost in peaceful thoughts of

95

home, there was a loud WHAP on his eardrums, followed instantly by a deafening explosion. It was at least ten seconds before Cass realized that someone had thrown a grenade down in the town. The sound had been contained and funnelled to him by the surrounding rock wall, leaving his ears ringing in his head. He crouched and looked over the parapet, trying to pinpoint the activity.

Someone was screaming in the streets. Cass's heart was pounding as the sound cut through the ringing in his ears. Then a high shrill voice shouted, "Taff's been hit. For Christsakes get an ambulance." There was the fear and anxiety of a close friend of the victim in that voice. Taff's mate had his pal's bloodied head resting on his knee, could see the terror and pain in the eyes. The screaming went on.

Cass whirred the handle of the field telephone and reported the incident to the control room.

"They need an ambulance," he said.

The operator at the other end acknowledged the request.

Cass went back to his surveillance of the scene below him. Boots were running on the streets now, and someone was shouting, "The bastard went down here, Sarge . . . " Cass gripped his rifle, wondering if the terrorists ever thought of climbing up the rockface at the back of town. They would come close to him if they did.

He never saw the ambulance arrive. Perhaps they took the wounded soldier out some other way, on a makeshift stretcher or in a Land-Rover? Within a very short while it had all gone quiet again. The town settled into peace once more. Whether the terrorist had been caught or not, Cass would probably never know. There had been no shots fired. He could not see any patrols now.

He remained alert after that, for a long while. Every sound had him jumping. This was fine while adrenaline surged through him, keeping him nervous, but once it had ceased to do its job he fell once more into apathy. The lapse into boredom became complete again, just twelve minutes before he was due to be relieved by the next sentry. Then some pretty fairy lights came up towards him from a dark corner of the town. He watched them, surprised and interested. Tinker Bells, all in a line, evenly spaced. Fireflies, migrating like geese.

There were chunky smacking sounds in the brickwork of the watchtower just below Cass's hand.

"SHIT!"

He dropped to the floor as the tracer rounds from some automatic weapon down in the streets continued to hack and whine at the tower. He accidentally knocked the telephone off its cradle, and only then remembered he could call someone. His hands trembled as he worked the handle.

"Control Centre," said a crackly voice.

"I'm being fired at," cried Cass.

"Who's being fired at?" enquired the voice, calmly.

"Me, you silly bastard!"

Then he realized they wanted a location, and gave them one.

By the time Control had phoned the radio shack flight sergeant, who had run up, breathless, to the tower, the shooting had stopped. Cass lay on the floor of the watchtower a long time after the flight sergeant had left him. He was still trembling when he was relieved, though the fear had gone away. When he entered the radio shack, he began to feel elated for some reason, as though someone had just given him a piece of wonderful news.

One of the intelligence officers, Flight Lieutenant Parkinson, nodded to him as he came through the door.

"Bit of activity out there tonight, eh Carson?"

"Yes sir." Cass put his rifle in the rack feeling as if he had won a battle single-handed.

"I don't expect it'll be the last," said Parkinson. "Probably step up now the gulli-gulli man's back in circulation."

Cass took a mug of tea from the Somali bearer and was about to go to the rest room when he stopped. Something clicked in

97

his head. He turned and said to the officer, who was now studying a message, "Gulli-gulli man, sir?"

The flight lieutenant looked up. "What? Oh, yes. One of the NLF bright sparks. Trained in Cairo by Nasser's boys. Disappeared for a while, upcountry we think, but it now looks like he's back." Parkinson waved the piece of paper in his hand. "Have to watch our arses till we catch the bugger. So far he's slipped the net."

"Does he have another name? I mean, that's just a codename for him, isn't it?"

"Sure. His real name is Abdulla Achmed, but we call him the gulli-gulli man because he's a bloody magician – disappears into thin air." Parkinson laughed, and then his eyes narrowed as he looked into Cass's face. "What's the matter, Carson?"

"Nothing, sir. This *terrorist*, was his father a clerk serving the British at one time?"

"You're remarkably well informed."

Cass waved his hand and turned away.

"Oh, I think I read it somewhere, maybe in one of the messages. I don't know. I thought I'd heard the name before."

"Well," said the intelligence officer, "we'll get him, eventually. Someone will give him to us. FLOSY would love to hand him over, or even eliminate him themselves. He's a bit of thorn in their side, too."

"Why do we say that, sir? *A thorn in their side?*"

The officer looked surprised.

"I don't know. Never thought about it. Something to do with Christ, I suppose. He was wounded in the side by a Roman soldier, when he was on the cross, wasn't he?"

"But by a spear. The thorns were on his head."

"Sure, then I don't know. Probably has its origins in some obscure tale. They usually do, these idioms."

"Thank you, sir."

The eyes narrowed again, slightly.

"That's okay, Carson. Go and have your tea now."

"Yes, I will."

Cass had only just sat down and taken a sip from his mug of tea when Parkinson appeared in the doorway. There was no one else in the rest room and the officer took the chair next to Cass.

"All right, man, what's your story?" asked Parkinson in a kindly voice.

"My story, sir?"

"Cut the 'sir' crap. I want to know how you were aware of Abdulla Achmed's father's profession."

"Isn't it common knowledge?"

"No, it's bloody well not, now stop playing games with me, Carson. The NLF aren't aware that we know who the gulli-gulli man is. He's always referred to by his codename. You've got some inside information there. If you *did* read it in a message, as you said, then I want to see the piece of paper."

Cass sighed.

"I was raised here, in Aden. My father was a sergeant armourer, in the RAF. Abdulla Achmed is a friend of mine – was – when we were teenagers."

Parkinson nodded. Like everyone else at the unit, he always dressed in civilian clothes. Cass had once seen him with his skin artificially darkened and wearing a *futa*, skullcap and khaki shirt, like an Arab. Parkinson and the two other intelligence officers were fluent in Arabic. It wasn't difficult to imagine this brown-eyed Englishman hanging around the *suq*, picking up snippets of information. Cass admired that, tremendously. Parkinson was an adult "Kim", passing for a local. He was the sort of man Heather might marry.

"I wish you'd told someone this sooner," Parkinson said.

"What, that I'd been raised in Aden? Not much to that, is there? Of course, if I'd known one of my best friends was a terrorist, I'd have spoken up."

"Would you? Just a few moments ago you found out, but I had to come to you, not the other way around."

"I was thinking about it. It was a bit of a shock."

99

"I'll accept that. Anyway, we might make use of it some time, now that I know." Parkinson sat back and folded his arms. "Does that bother you at all? Do you have divided loyalties?"

Cass flashed him an angry look.

"Of course I do, what do you think?" Then he remembered who he was talking to. "I'm sorry, sir. That probably makes me sound like some sort of traitor to you, but I don't think of it that way."

Parkinson shook his head.

"Nothing of the sort. Good Lord, man, you think you're the only one? I went to Cambridge with two of the blighters I shopped in Malaya. Look, I'm not going to use your friendship to flush him out, or anything like that. I can't see how that can be done, and despite your loyalty to him the gulli-gulli man is a ruthless terrorist. He certainly wouldn't put himself in danger over an old friend, especially if the friend's British. Believe me, if it ever came to a choice I'm willing to bet my grandmother's soul that he'd sacrifice *any* childhood friend if it meant furthering his cause. Where you might be useful is if we catch him alive. That's all."

Cass nodded.

"All right."

Parkinson stared at him for a long time before saying, "You're a funny one, Carson. Where did you go to school? You don't seem like the run-of-the-mill airman to me."

"I had a good education, eventually, here in Aden. Khormaksar School. My family was set on an air force career though, and I was sent to Cosford . . . "

"Tech training?"

"Yes. Came out a Telegraphist II and then specialized in the reception of high-speed Morse. I never took any school-leaving exams, no GCEs. You couldn't at a secondary modern, which was what I went back to when we returned to England."

"So, you resent not going to grammar or public school?"

"I suppose I do, a little. You see, the local education authority

100

was prejudiced against service children, because they took up spaces in the grammar school which they were going to vacate within a short period of time. So not many of us got through the eleven-plus, if you see what I mean."

"You think they favoured the locals? You don't think it's just sour grapes on your part, for failing the exam, and now you're getting a little paranoid?"

Cass shook his head.

"Frankly, sir, I'll never know. One of the fathers, a squadron leader, kicked up a fuss later and they found the results *had* been weighted in favour of local children – but it was too late for me. I was already in Aden by that time. My parents couldn't do much about it, being so far away from Britain. It's possible I put up a lousy performance, but I don't think so. I'm not exceptionally bright, but I know I could have made university – perhaps not Cambridge – but one of the newer ones, Leeds or Canterbury."

"Don't you have a go at me, just because I'm a Cambridge graduate," smiled Parkinson.

Cass smiled back.

"I'll try not to."

Parkinson put a hand on his shoulder. "You can still get to university, you know."

"I intend to. I'm taking correspondence courses."

"Good for you. Well, thanks for the chat. I'm sure we'll talk again, before too long. Keep your nose clean."

"Thanks, sir."

Parkinson got up and went to the doorway of the rest room, before turning round again.

"You're not furthering your education because you want a commission, are you?"

"If I ever get a degree, sir, the last thing I'll use it for is to become an officer."

"Is that a put-down?"

"No, it's just me. I don't know what I'm doing in the RAF in the first place. 'In de footsteps of de father, go de little son, an'

101

he never did do nuthin' that his daddy didn't done.' Quote from 'Ole Masser'. I got it from *Scouting For Boys* – I've never seen the original. I'm almost ready to step out of my father's tracks."

"I'm betting on it," said Parkinson, and left Cass to his tea and his thoughts. His little speeches sounded braver than he actually felt. His stomach churned when he thought of going for an interview for a place at university, even though he had heard they looked favourably on mature students. Could he do it? After an initial handicap, he had caught up with Dix at school, had left him behind in some subjects, English literature, biology. Dix went, to Cardiff. One of his last letters to Cass was as a Fresher. Heather went, to Edinburgh. Only Abdulla and himself had left study behind at fifteen. Now here they were, the pair of them, shooting at each other. Was that how it worked? If you didn't go for further education, you took the road of violence? That was silly. Parkinson had been to Cambridge. Probably went to a good public school. Cass didn't mind that, so long as men like Parkinson did not form an elite, to keep out the riffraff. Block the plebs like himself from good careers. Did they do that? Some of them did it naturally. They did it like breathing or sleeping. They kept out the lower orders and became politicians themselves, making decisions, like keeping the British in Aden too long.

"God, you're a bitter inverted snob, Oliver Carson," he said aloud.

Parkinson poked his head around the door.

"Didn't want to say anything myself, Carson, but you've hit the nail on the head there."

Damn, thought Cass, there were spies everywhere.

10

Mum and Dad were going to the sergeants' mess fancy dress ball and came to see me in my bedroom before they left. Dad was covered by a white sheet with eyeholes and had around his neck a string of empty miniature whisky and gin bottles. The sign on his back read: DEPARTED SPIRITS. I thought that was pretty good. Mum, though, was dressed as a gypsy and looked so much the part she scared me. Even though her features were of course uncovered, I couldn't recognize my mother in her. She was dark, sinister, and had she cursed me in fun I think I would have died right then and there, from sheer funk. I thought afterwards about natives of primitive tribes who turned their faces to the wall and drifted into death, once the witch doctor had pronounced sentence on them, and empathized with them completely.

After they had left the house and I heard Said going to bed I got up and dressed in shorts and T-shirt, and climbed out of the window. Then I made my way to the *chokidar*'s hut at the back entrance to Khormaksar camp, where I waited for Dix. We were going down to the beach to look for turtles. It was a clear starry night with enough moon to illuminate the sands.

The *chokidar* in his role as nightwatchman chatted to me in Arabic for a while until we had both exhausted my vocabulary. He offered me tea from his can and I took a few sips out of politeness. I asked if I could look at his *jambia*, the broad dagger that most Arabs carried in their belts as a symbol of manhood, usually heavily ornamented with silver wire. Before I had seen one of these knives drawn from its sheath I had thought they were almost U-shaped, like the sheath itself. That was the fault of the comic-book artists who drew wicked-looking caricatures of the blades, always wielded by Arabs in flowing garments and sporting black pointed beards. The blades no more filled the sheaths than the feet of viziers filled those spiral-toed sandals they were supposed to wear.

The *chokidar* let me have a few stabs in the air at an imaginary opponent before grinning and retrieving his dagger. He showed me a creased old photo of his wife and child and I made the right noises in response. We got on well together, the European children and the Arabs who stood at the gates of the Empire's establishments. It seemed to matter little to them that we were the sons and daughters of their colonial masters. It certainly did not matter to us that they were fierce and savage tribesmen recruited from tiny lost villages in the interior, tame only during their brief spell of service. We laughed and joked with one another, easy in each other's company, never finding offence where there was none. Perhaps that was because neither of us cared about loss of face? Once pride entered the relationship, imaginary slights and insults swept in like sandstorms to erode any trust.

We told the *chokidars* stories of snowbound winters in Yorkshire and Fife, and they told us tales of the Rub'al Khālī, the empty quarter of the Arabian Desert. We exchanged secrets of our individual cultures, amazed at how the other side lived. We made pacts as easily as shaking hands.

Dix came out of the darkness, saying, "Hello Choki, *tammam?*"

"*Aiwa,*" grinned my very good friend, "*tammam.*"

After that, Dix and I made our way to Khormaksar beach, where the turtles were laying their eggs. We walked along the moonlit shore towards Crater, listening to the sounds of the ocean and jumping over hermit crabs that raced for the sea on our approach. The air had a rich warmth to it that adults would have called uncomfortable but which we thought balmy.

"My mum got a letter from Maddy Swanson's mum today," said Dix. "They've been back in England two days. She says it's cold."

"I remember that," I said, "it being cold."

"She says Maddy's gettin' married."

"Oh, because of the baby I suppose."

That subject exhausted, for what it was worth to the selfish world of youth, we turned to the turtles.

"Did you bring the torch?" I asked.

Dix flashed the device once in answer.

"Good," I said.

When we got to the end of the bay, where the turtles came ashore, we saw three of them humping the flat sands. We watched while the great lugubrious creatures laid their eggs in shallow holes above the high-tide mark, flippered the sand to cover them, shuffled around on the top to hide the spot where their young would be born, then ponderously dragged their heavy shells down to the water's edge. Once in the waves the turtles became graceful, almost birdlike in their movements through the submarine world of fish.

The turtle is not a caring parent, preferring a heigh-ho life to the responsibilities of raising a family. Dad is nowhere to be seen, his job having ended with the business of conception. Mum does not fuss over her eggs, nor does she return at the moment of birth to assist her offspring. She swims away into the deep ocean and leaves around eighty little ones to fend for themselves. If they survive egg-hunters in the shape of humans and pi-dogs, they burst out of the warm womb of sand and make a dash for the sea, their soft-shelled bodies exposed to the gulls and kite hawks. Those tiny few that reach the ocean are pursued and eaten by carnivorous fish. One of the newly hatched creatures might escape, to mature into an adult. A fully-grown turtle is literally one of a hundred, its siblings all dead, and its life adventures rival those of Sinbad or the Thief of Baghdad.

Dix dug up some of the eggs, which were like slick ping-pong balls with soft shells, and we toyed with taking them home to eat. However, experiments of this kind always ended in battles with our parents so we reburied the eggs and promised ourselves we would return for the hatching, to drive away predators and assist the helpless turtlettes. Such is the optimism of youth, that it believes it can pinpoint in time the moment of birth.

We got back to our respective beds before the parents came home, jolly after their evening of boozing under their various disguises, and I was asleep before the giggles and whispers ascended the stairs.

The next day we were going camping with the scouts at Sheik Othman Gardens. I packed my gear under the unwanted supervision of my brothers, who barely escaped without thick lips for their trouble, then joined Abdulla and Dix at the pick-up point outside the BOAC offices. The coach came, and we were on our way, excitement buzzing in our breasts.

We followed the shoreline until we came to the saltpans, where seawater was wind-pumped into dammed fields and left to evaporate, leaving the salt to be scraped into containers. This area of Aden reminded me a little of the East Anglian saltings I had left behind in England: stretches of white flatland where the waders came to feast. There had been snipes and herons in England too, but here there were also flamingoes, sometimes in their thousands, a haze of pink on the still waters of the fields. Occasionally one or two pelicans waddled into the pans. These birds, like the turtles, looked ungainly when walking but in their own environment were as graceful as angels. Pelicans do not, as their beaks may suggest, scoop fish from the water during a horizontal flight. They circle above the sea until they spot a suitable shoal below them, then they plummet as if made of lead. Their wings fold back on impact with the water, and for a moment they are lost in a chrysanthemum of spray. Then they emerge a moment later, triumphantly, born again from the waves. I never tired of watching them.

"Right," said Skip, "pitch your tents, lay out your kit and I'll come and inspect in one hour."

We did as we were told, erecting the four-man tents on grass much coarser than any I had ever seen in England. Around us were the Gardens, full of palm trees, flowered walks and picnic spots. We chose a corner near a bed of red and white oleander. Our fourth man was Ali, a cousin of Abdulla. The four of us worked quite well together until Dix and I got into one of our heated arguments over fauna.

"Don't go for a crap in the middle of the night," said Dix, "or you might get bitten by a puff adder. They're deadly poisonous."

"You don't get puff adders here," I said, the panic welling up inside me.

"You get puff adders, horned vipers, 'n' whipsnakes," said Dix, positively.

"You don't get puff adders, do you?" I asked Ali, who was helping me with the poles.

He shrugged, his eyes going from one to the other of us. It always worried him when we argued hotly.

"You-get-puff-adders," said Dix, raising his voice.

"You-bloody-don't! Puff adders are African," I yelled.

"Don't swear at me. You wait and see then. They like to come in the tent to snuggle up to warm bodies. See tonight."

I suddenly felt very miserable and wanted to be at home. I have a fear of poisonous snakes which I believe is entirely rational: the damn things can kill you with one bite after all. There's nothing irrational about a fear of death.

Abdulla whispered to me, "I sleep near the tent-flaps. I kill any snake coming in." I knew he was trying to help, but snakes could come under the walls of the tent, from any direction.

"Puff adders are African," I repeated, almost in tears.

That night we lay in bed and talked until the early hours, when the others fell asleep one by one. I lay awake, sweating inside my pinned-together army blankets, listening for slithering

107

sounds. Round about two o'clock, I heard something on Dix's side of the tent.

Please God, I prayed, let it bite Dix and not me.

There was a snuffling sound and the tent bulged inwards just above Dix's head. My heart was thudding in my chest and I had a catch in my throat. The bulge began moving backwards and forwards along the wall of the tent. It was a blunt rounded shape, such as might have been produced by the head of a particularly thick snake.

Finally I found my voice.

"PUFF ADDER!" I shrieked.

Abdulla leapt to his feet and shot out into the night, his sheathknife in his hand. Dix sat up and stared with round eyes into the darkness. Ali hardly moved.

A few moments later Abdulla pushed back the flap of the tent and beckoned me. I went out cautiously as Dix was still searching for his glasses amongst the array of toiletries, socks and underpants scattered around the tent. Outside the moonlight flowed through the palms and I followed Abdulla's arm to where he was pointing.

A few yards away a gazelle was grazing. It had obviously bolted when I yelled, but had halted again, being one of those creatures who had come out of the desert some time ago, and was now semi-tame, living in and around the Gardens. Abdulla grinned, and slapped my shoulder. I nodded, feeling foolish. We went back in the tent and Dix, still looking for his glasses, said, "What was it?"

"Puff adder," said Abdulla.

"Yeah," I said, "you were right, Dix. The place must be crawling with them."

"Get away," Dix said.

"You don't believe us," I said, in a voice full of disgust.

Dix was cautious.

"I dunno. Maybe."

We left it at that. The funny thing was, I was able to get to

108

sleep afterwards, even though I still had not established whether Arabian puff adders were fact or fiction. It seemed that a false alarm had been enough to stifle my fears, at least for the time it took to fall asleep.

The following morning the Moslems were up first to say their prayers, then the rest of us crawled out, glad that the Christian God was not so demanding. Once we were all around the camp-fire we made the traditional dampers and twist – simply dough cakes on platters and dough snakes wound round greensticks – and had them for breakfast with eggs and beans. Everything had bits of twig and grass in it, but that was part of camping. I missed the smell of bacon frying over a wood fire, but since we had Moslems in the group we never took any kind of pig meat with us on a camp. Skip asked who was doing all the yelling during the night and when he didn't get an answer he told the two patrol leaders, of the Kestrels and Eagles, that they would be responsible for discipline after lights-out.

At ten o'clock we were driven down to the beach. Skip had hired a dhow to take us out for a sail, and we were all very excited about it. We clambered aboard a craft that looked a genuine antique. Arabs had been building dhows just like this one since the Roman Empire had started clearing the seas of buccaneers. The Adeni sailors escaped this early policing, of course, there being no canal linking the Mediterranean and Red Seas in those days. They remained pirates until the British Empire came along to do the job.

The captain of our *boom* was a Somali, the blackest and most dignified man I had ever seen. He stood close to the mast the whole time, moving only his lips when he was giving an order. There had been some dignified men with the Queen, when she had visited Aden four weeks previously, but none like this man. He was as straight as the mast itself, his features as handsomely set as those on the Roman statues in the British Museum, and his hair looked as if it were made from salt. He was a Roman Emperor, a Severus, born too late and in the wrong class. His

109

profile would have had Parthian archers quaking behind their bows, had there been any left after the first Severus had finished with them. So far as I was concerned, our own Queen wouldn't have gone far wrong if she'd chosen this man as a husband, rather than the Duke who was good-looking enough in his way but no match for this aristocratic sea captain.

Queen Elizabeth's visit to Aden had been a non-event so far as Dix and I were concerned. The only glimpse we caught of her was when she came to lay the foundation stone to the new hospital. The scout groups lined the route, but all I saw was a little white hat sitting on the head of a small woman in the back of a moving car. She was there and gone.

The dhow put out to sea with scouts running all over the deck and the captain standing still as marble in the middle of it all. There were four crew to the dhow and they worked like stink until the lateen sail cracked full of wind and we went ploughing into the Indian Ocean. In no time at all there were fifteen scouts, English, Arab, Somali and Indian, throwing up the dampers and twist they had taken on board at breakfast. The dhow rose and fell on the swell, as light as a cork, and the pitch and roll of the vessel was dramatic enough to make even Skip go pale and hang on to the rigging.

The idea was for the dhow's captain to sail along the coast to the harbour, circumnavigating Crater and Little Aden. I clung on to the rail, staring bleakly at the craggy form of Crater as we dipped alongside Khormaksar beach, and wished I had gone catfish fishing instead.

"I don't like this," I said to Dix.

"Don't talk to me," was the muffled answer.

Abdulla had given up all hope of saving face and was lying full length on the deck, staring at the sky, as if he expected help to arrive from above very soon. We sailed for the first promontory jutting from Crater, and went around it.

It was calmer once we were round the *ras*, and as we entered the harbour we began to recover a little. We passed a moored

Union-Castle ship, up from the Cape, and then a P&O liner which stared down at us imperiously from a great bladed height. By the time we reached Little Aden and the new oil refinery site, we were feeling much better. Then we hit open sea again.

Skip asked the Somali captain to take us to the shore as quickly as possible, but the man was too honourable to give us less than our money's worth. He insisted on the full journey.

Finally, soaked with spray, we came about and began the return trip. Once again the harbour was a sea of tranquillity, then out the other side again, into choppy waters. By this time we were getting our sea legs and schoolboy dares were being flung tauntingly into schoolboy faces.

"Bet you can't climb the rigging," said Dix.

"I can," I said, "but Skip'll go bonkers."

"Good excuse," Dix cried, "but I think you're scared you'll fall off. Watch me."

He waited until Skip and the captain were talking and paying attention to each other, then he pulled himself up on the rail and inched his way up a sheet until he was over the deck. Then he let his legs dangle, before dropping down at my feet.

"How about that then?" he said triumphantly.

"Not very high," I said, foolishly.

Dix folded his arms. "Okay then, let's see *high*."

Having let myself in for it, I could do nothing but climb. I pulled myself up on to the wet rail the way Dix had done, but instead of grabbing the taut sheet which led to the corner of the lateen sail, I took hold of a sheet going out and up to the end of the boom, out over the water.

"I'm going to touch the boom," I said, my legs trembling as I began to move along the rope, "*then* we'll see ... "

I was about ten feet out from the rail when I heard Skip's voice screaming at me. Glancing down I could see the white-green water slipping past at a terrifying rate. There was no thought of going back though. I had to do what I had set out to do. *If you start something, always finish it.* Adults instil these things

111

in you as inflexible rules, then they wonder why you stick to them in times when discretion is needed. They don't say, *use your initiative*, they give you something that flips easily off the tongue which they don't have to explain, expecting it to cover every contingency.

I continued climbing along the rope. Skip had stopped shouting now. I suppose he realized that yelling would do no good at all and might make me lose concentration. The sheet was wet and rubbed the backs of my legs, where I had them wrapped around it, every time I pulled myself a bit further along. Whenever I bent my head back to see where the end of the boom was, it looked just as far away as it had done at the start of the climb. All I wanted to do was just touch it, just brush it with my fingers, then I could slip back along the sheet again.

Finally, I was almost there. I stretched out an arm, aware of a couple of dozen pairs of eyes on me. My fingertips touched wood. Then the boat yawed violently. My body swung sideways. The hand clutching the sheet was wrenched free by my weight. I was looking upwards, into the blue. For a moment I thought I was falling into the sky. Then my body struck cold water and I went beneath the foam.

Immediately I surfaced, I was aware of the strong current. It swept me in a curve, threatening to take me out to open sea. I struck out for the dhow, which I kept losing sight of as the swell rose above me. I began to swallow water, now a little frightened by the dramatic movements of the ocean. There are mighty forces at work in open waters, too strong for a young boy to cope with, even if he is a good swimmer. I was soon tired, but the knowledge that the boat would be turning back helped me keep my head.

My arms felt as if they were being torn from their sockets. I paused to rest them, treading water, wondering where the dhow had got to. Perhaps they couldn't see me, below the waves? Then I noticed something long and black out of the corner of my eye, just before it was lost in the swell, and another fear rushed through me. The waters around Aden were notorious for sharks.

112

One only had to stand at the end of the bays, to see the sleek shapes moving amongst the brain coral. Admittedly I had only seen small sharks near the shore, but here I was out at sea. To my twelve-year-old mind it did not seem illogical that the deeper the water became, the bigger the fish that swam in it.

I tried to lie absolutely still, having been told that splashing around on the surface would be likely to attract sharks, whose radar was primed for fish in distress. It was not an easy task, because I also had to stay afloat. The waves kept slopping over my face, the salt stinging my eyes.

Then it was there, on top of me, the black, blunt-nosed shape. I felt something clutch at my shirt, wrench me from the water. It was a few seconds before I realized what was happening. I was in a fishing canoe: one of those roughly-hewn, simple but solid craft, a descendant of the log dugout. There were needles sticking in my chest and my face was cheek to cheek with something cold and spongy. I had to get my breath before I moved. When some strength finally returned to my limbs I found I was lying on a pile of fish. The needles were sharp dorsal fins and my face was stuck in the fleshy underside of an octopus. As I tried to get up, I was pushed back down firmly by a calloused foot. It seemed I had to endure my relationship with the eels, fish and octopuses just a bit longer. The fisherman was concerned that I might capsize his canoe. They were not all dead of course. I could feel some of them moving under my belly.

When he finally let me stand up, the fisherman was holding some net rigging thrown over the side of the dhow. Hands reached down and I was hauled on board.

Skip gave the fisherman five pounds. He gave me the biggest dressing-down I had ever received outside the family. I knew I deserved it and decided I was lucky he didn't mention throwing me out of the group on my ear. When we reached the shore I suggested to him that we need not tell my mother. I believed that was to his advantage as well as mine, because most mothers consider their offspring to be in safe hands with a scoutmaster.

113

Skip would hear none of it. My parents were to be informed the next day, Sunday, when they visited the scout camp with the other mums and dads.

That night puff adders were the furthest thing from my mind. To the lads, of course, I was a bit of a hero, but I expected my mother to steam from the ears when she heard about my escapades.

11

Of course Mum was angry (and Dad pretended to be) but the dust settled more quickly than was expected. Part of the reason for this was the shocking news that the Arab beggar outside the Khormaksar camp gates had been murdered. He had been found early that morning, his face battered to pulp. One of the hardwood legs of his bed had been broken off and used as the murder weapon. The corpse had slithered down the tilted raffia-sprung frame and was found in a half-sitting position. The beggar's only possession, his water-bottle, was missing.

Was it possible that he had been killed for his water-bottle? That hardly seemed likely. It had only been an ordinary bottle, at one time containing lemonade, covered in wet rags to keep the contents cool. Still, there were some very poor people around. Skip knew a family upcountry who owned just a kettle. *A whole family and their only possession was a tin kettle.* Maybe the killer had come out of the desert terribly thirsty, and the beggar had refused him a drink? *That* was possible. The desert came right up to our backdoors. Perhaps some tribesman who had wandered in off the sands, desperate for a drink, had gone crazy?

My mother's interest in the affair stemmed not from the beggar himself, but from the possible repercussions of his death. She was afraid there would be rioting among the various cultures that shared the barren rocks of our peninsula.

"The Arabs think it was a racial killing," she told Skip, "and they're blaming the Somalis. There's already been some trouble near the airport – Arabs and Somalis, fighting. It's happened before, you know."

The Somalis were a minority group in Aden.

"The rock apes were called in this morning," she added after a pause, "and they walked between them. The locals were throwing stones. Not pebbles, but stones as big as your fist. One of them hit our house. The rock apes fixed bayonets before they went in to sort it out."

"Rock apes" was an affectionate name the airmen gave to the RAF regiment, the soldiers of the Royal Air Force, whose duties included guarding airfields and keeping general order within air-force jurisdiction. The actual simian rock apes lived on the island of Gibraltar, on top of the famous hill, but somewhere in their past the RAF regiment had earned the same nickname. The regiment said they were called rock apes because they were as agile and athletic as monkeys, but other airmen believed the ratio of muscle to brain power had a lot to do with it.

The fact that the rock apes had fixed bayonets was meant to impress Mum's listener. The inference was that, like a Gurkha's kukri, the bayonet was not unsheathed unless it was going to draw blood. The problem there would be the bayonet itself, which in those days had a rounded blade with no cutting edge, like a marlinspike. I imagined the rock apes, stolid lads from the Shires, pricking their fingers with the point of the weapons before they were able to return them to their sheaths.

"My cook-bearer's afraid to go out," said Mum, as if Said were a precocious child left in her care. She was getting used to having a servant and had adopted the special tone of speech general to British wives when talking of their domestic staff. It was a tone which mixed reverence (if you respected your cook's creations, it could only reflect good on yourself) and condescension (he was, after all, only a native bearer) with complete success. That the wives could mingle two such opposing views in one tone was an astonishing and remarkable feat of vocalization. "He's absolutely terrified he'll be stoned to death on the street – or

116

stabbed with one of those nasty curved things the Arabs carry. I've told him to stay indoors. I don't know where I'd get another cook-bearer like him, even though like most Somalis he's got his faults."

Skip raised his eyebrows at the last sentence, but wisely kept quiet. My mother could be a bit of a tartar if criticized by anyone outside the family. Or inside, for that matter.

To me, she administered one of her severe set-downs.

"You're *never* going on a boat again, do you hear?"

I imagined myself, middle-aged and greying, being invited on board the yacht of a rich friend.

Sorry, Archie, my mum's forbidden me *ever* to set foot on another boat.

"Yes Mum," I said.

"I mean it mind!" she snapped, detecting a glint of amusement in my eyes. "*Not ever!*"

The cartoons in my head became more ludicrous.

Sorry, ferryman, you'll have to take these other dead souls across the Styx without me, my mum says I must *never* get in a boat.

"Yes Mum."

The rest of the day was spent in demonstrations for the benefit of the parents, ending with a wide game and finally the spectacle of them watching us trying to kill ourselves playing British bull-dog. This was a game where one set of boys formed themselves into a human wall, then another set of boys charged at them, leapt into the air and came down heavily on the waiting bodies. It was a deliberate attempt to crush the opponents and force them to collapse. Feet, elbows, knees, fists, all were permissible in this schoolboy equivalent of a gladiatorial spectacle. It was a game that was supposed to be character-forming, and was probably introduced into Britain by some sadistic public-school master. It was certainly responsible for creating certain *types* of character, extreme character, making hooligans of some, and nervous wrecks of others.

And the parents? Instead of being sickened by this violence, and rushing screaming on to the playing field to save their young, the parents of Aden clapped politely whenever another lout charged and hurled himself full force, boots first, through the air at the wall of human bodies. It's my belief that British bulldog is actually a very early game, borrowed by some savage tribe such as the Picts or the Iceni, from a central European horde like the Vandals.

As usual, I came away with several blue-black bruises, which my mother fussed over with gentle fingers while talking to a neighbour, and then promptly forgot. In those days boys were expected to toughen themselves for the adult world with every method of physical self-abuse short of suicide. Those without scabbed knees, cut lips or bloody noses were, in the words of Mr Cootley, "lily-livered loons".

Afterwards Abdulla introduced me to his father, who looked very grand in a turban of some sort, a white smock and a black gown over the top. He shook my hand enthusiastically and said he had enjoyed the show very much. "Your son's very good at tricks," I said, "he's a real magician," and the father laughed.

I took Abdulla aside afterwards.

"Bring your Uncle Hussein to my house next Wednesday evening," I said. "It's my parents' evening in."

"What for?" asked Abdulla.

"Just bring him," I hissed. "Make him carry a fishing-net."

Abdulla shrugged and looked mystified, but gave me a nod in the end, then went to join his father. I saw his dad place a hand on his head and say something to him. Then with one arm around Ali and the other around Abdulla, the older man left the scene. The only people who had spoken to him, apart from me and Dix, were Skip and my mum. I was pleased with my mother for that.

The next day we were back at school. In two months from that day I would be thirteen years of age. I was beginning to make up for the lost years at Felixstowe Primary and Secondary, where I had learned about the Romans – names of roads like Fosse Way and Ermine Street – but not much else. My timestables always came in useful, of course, and I could chant you a hundred hymns and hardly falter. Taught by rote, one never forgets.

Mick and Mac were the rebels of this classroom and I was one of the good guys for once. My last end-of-term school report gave me A's or B's for everything except music, which had the phrase, *Cannot sing*, written alongside the C+. I don't think I even deserved the *plus*, since I couldn't play any instrument except a bugle, which hardly counted, and my voice always found a tuneless middle ground between two pitches.

The thing I liked doing best was reciting poetry. I began to learn poems the way I had learned hymns, storing them up to use at appropriate times. Dix and Heather used to taunt me, calling me a pleb because while they wanted to play classical music on Heather's record player, I preferred Eddie Cantor singing songs like, *"Way down the river he would row, just him and Chloe . . . "* I would lose ground with Heather to Dix, until I had the chance to quote T. Campbell's version of "The Maid of Neidpath", or William Soutar's "The Tryst", which in the future was to encapsulate my thoughts of Heather completely: *"Sae luely, luely cam she in, sae luely she was gaen; and wi' her all my simmer days, like they had never been . . . "* With these, and other romantic Scottish poems, I would surge ahead again. Those Ayrshire eyes would fill with Highland mist and nothing Dix could do would take them from my face in times like those. In class I would woo Mrs Gower with lines from Wilfred Owen or one of the other trench poets. It wasn't all artfulness. I genuinely liked poetry the way I liked climbing up the crags of Jebel Shamsan at sunrise, or watching a dhow slip away towards Africa. There was a mystique about all these things that touched my soul. I had already written a story about a woman flyer (inspired by Amy Johnson) which had won me a school prize.

For the first time in my life I began to gain some academic

119

confidence, though I knew that when we were sent home to England I would be back in secondary school, where woodwork and metalwork was encouraged, and poetry and creative writing was neglected completely. There would be no school-leaving exams for me. I would be out at work at fifteen and my family would be more than surprised if I expected it to be otherwise. I was lucky to be in a place where the classes were so small there was no sense in creaming off the excellence. The sticklebacks like me were in the same stream as the trout. I didn't want to go back to my old scummy pond, amongst pike who regarded learning with suspicion and contempt, and saw to it that any leaning in this direction was punished savagely. My only hope lay in evening classes or some form of education to be gained while out at work.

On Monday, before school started, Arabs and Somalis confronted one another across the maidan. They were about a football-pitch width apart, two lines of them, jeering and taunting each other. Some of them had brought stones, which were thrown with great force. Occasionally poorly-aimed missiles landed near to our feet, as we stood waiting to go into school. Mick and Mac began throwing them back again, one at the line of Arabs, the other (to be fair) at the Somalis. More stones began to come our way, some of them deliberately aimed at us.

"Don't be stupid, Mick," said Heather, as he heaved a lump of concrete back at the thrower.

"Come off it, the bleeders are throwin' at us!"

Dix said, "They think you're taking sides."

"I am," said Mac, "*our* side."

At that moment Mrs Gower came out, all of a twitter, and began to usher us inside the classroom. Despite her protests, we immediately went to the windows to watch, and saw the rock apes arrive. They dropped out of two trucks and formed a hollow square, kneeling, their rifles pointing outwards like bristles. Inside the square was a sergeant with a megaphone, an officer, and an Arab in a magistrate's gown.

120

The sergeant bawled, "Fix," long pause, "bayonets!"

Hands flashed down to belts, twisted slightly, then came up with silver spikes flashing in the early morning sunlight. There were impressive-sounding *clicks*, and hands went back to the stocks of Lee-Enfields.

The men rose to a command and began walking at tortoise pace, in their hollow-square formation, between the two warring lines, daring anyone to throw a brick. Someone did. It missed a rock ape's head by a centimetre. The perpetrator ran away, to the rear of the crowd of Arabs. The sergeant bawled, the square stopped moving. For a few minutes everyone just stood and perspired. There were no more bricks thrown. The square tortoise began moving again.

When it reached the point where they were midway down between the two opposing lines the rock apes were ordered to halt, then load, which resulted in another impressive clicking of bolts. Two men ran out from the hollow square carrying a roll of barbed wire. This they opened up before the line of Arabs. A second roll was produced by two more men, who ran this out before the Somalis. The four airmen returned to the middle of the hollow square, clearly relieved to be inside the rifles once again. End on, from our classroom viewpoint, going left to right were: a line of Arabs, a barbed-wire barrier, the hollow square of rock apes, a barbed-wire barrier, a line of Somalis. It was all tremendously exciting.

"If either of 'em charge," whispered Mac, in a voice full of wishful thinking, "they'll be shot to bits." He just wanted to see something happen in the way of violence and death.

A banner was held up above the hollow square. It was written in English and Arabic. In English it read: DISPERSE IMMEDIATELY. Then the sergeant handed the megaphone to the magistrate, who began what sounded like a litany, but was probably good advice to the potential combatants.

The Arabs sat down.

The Somalis sat down.

121

The rock apes remained where they were.

We were called to lessons.

All through the morning we heard the megaphone being used. Sometimes the speaker used English, sometimes Arabic. At break-time we were not allowed outside, but we saw housewives ferrying drinks to everyone, regardless of race or creed, as they all waited it out on the maidan. It was a bit like Ramadan, the Islamic fast month, when everyone lolled around looking limp and pathetic.

By the time we were due home from school, there were only two or three Arabs and as many Somalis. They had drifted away in small knots, keeping the balance even until the end. The poor rock apes were in the worst shape, having spent all morning out in the open, the sun beating down with over a hundred degrees Fahrenheit on their heads. Finally, they broke their hollow square and chased away the remaining dissidents, before dispersing themselves.

To my knowledge, no one ever discovered the identity of the murderer of the old beggar.

That evening we discussed the day's events as usual on Heather's veranda. Her brother Brian was there too, but since he was reading a *Batman* comic he hardly counted.

Heather was wearing a flower-patterned frock and had her plaits tied together in a loop behind her neck. She sat on the veranda top step with her arms locked around her knees and rocked back and forth as she spoke.

"Well, I know you boys found it exciting," she said, "but I was a wee bit anxious, I have to admit."

"They didn't have any ammunition," said Dix, hardly bothering to disguise the disgust in his voice.

"How do you mean?" I asked.

"I mean they didn't have any rounds in their rifles. I heard my dad talking to your dad, Cass. The rock apes only had their bayonets."

"But I heard them load their guns with bullets," said Heather.

122

Like most boys of our age and background, Dix and I were sticklers when it came to the use of military jargon, but would not have dared to correct Heather's mistakes. A *rifle* was of course never referred to as a gun, nor a *round* as a bullet. We said nothing, however. Had it been anyone else, or each other, we would have jumped down throats to put it right. As rival beaus in our chaste medieval romance we had to be extremely careful to keep the geometric shape of our triangle equal. If one of us were to leave, her parents would have put an end to the gatherings. Two parallel lines would never have been permitted to meet. Heather was far too young to have a *real* boyfriend, and it was only because we were three *chums*, like a trio from an Enid Blyton novel, that we were allowed to meet so often.

Brian, forever failing as an indulgent brother when it came to Heather's errors, looked up from his *Batman* comic and said, "Dumbo," but did not bother to elaborate. Neither did Heather bother to question her area of ignorance, having learned in her thirteen years on the earth that boys made the silliest fusses over the stupidest things.

"That was a trick," said Dix, "to work the bolt as if they was loading their ... their ... " he wanted to be the perfect gentleman, defer to her misuse of military language, but his chivalry was finally overwhelmed by his Prussian sense of preciseness, "their *rifles*."

"In that case I think it was jolly brave of them," said Heather.

I was about to point out that the Arabs and Somalis were only armed with stones, but thought better of it.

"We nearly had a Mau-Mau situation here," Dix said. "Like with General China in Kenya."

General China was one of Jomo Kenyatta's Mau-Mau terrorists, killing white farmers just a short distance away over the Indian Ocean. We were of course on the side of the colonials, thinking the Mau-Mau were thieves and murderers, biting the hand that fed them. But General China had taken our fancy. We were fascinated by him because of his ability to evade the authorities. We had a grudging respect for someone bearing such a swashbuckling name.

"Nuts," said Brian, still absorbed in his comic.

"It was a pretty close thing, anyway," I chipped in, anxious to set them straight on my own assessment of the situation. "I don't know what would have happened if the locals had attacked the school. We would have been in serious trouble."

"Piddle," remarked Brian.

I had had enough of our girlfriend's younger brother.

"What do you know about it?" I asked him haughtily.

Still he did not look up.

"Me? Well I know one thing, Mick and Mac Gophner would have knocked their blocks off, if they'd have got within ten yards of the school. They're barbarians, those two. Send 'em to Kenya, is what I say. They'll catch General China in two days and roast him over a slow fire on the third."

None of us said very much, after that.

On Wednesday evening my middle brother Richie answered the door and then called me.

"It's Abdulla," he yelled, "an' some old man."

I went to the door, and there on our veranda stood Abdulla and his uncle. Hussein had a fishing-net, one of those circular casting nets with weights around the hem. This piece of fisherman's equipment was draped in an unlikely fashion over his left arm. He almost looked the part. I reached forward and shifted the net from his arm to his shoulder, then I yelled for my mother.

She came to the door, her arms covered in flour up to her elbows. She was teaching Said to make sticky buns. She held out her arms in front of her like a Moslem suppliant.

"What is it?" she asked, her eyes flicking from me to the two Arabs, using the voice she used when people call at the door trying to sell something.

"This is the fisherman that saved me the other day."

"What?" She looked confused.

"You know, when I fell off the dhow, with Skip and the scouts. This man came in a canoe and rescued me. I'd be dead otherwise. Drowned if he hadn't come along. Or got by the sharks."

"Oh," she said, light entering her eyes, "I'll give him some money if he waits a minute."

"He'd rather have a job," I said.

She looked at me.

"What sort of a job?"

"Any sort. You could get him a job through your place, couldn't you?"

She seemed a little vague.

"I suppose so."

"Well, I think that would be good, wouldn't it? I mean he saved my life after all. I'm a good swimmer and all that, but the currents out there are pretty vicious."

"Oh, all right," she said, obviously still wondering what to do with her powdered hands, now holding them awkwardly as if she had been caught carrying them from one place to another. "Tell him to come and see me at the office next Monday. I'm sure we can hire him for something."

When she had gone, I turned to Abdulla.

"You heard that?" I grinned.

He was looking a little shocked.

"You lied to your mother," he said.

That wiped the grin off my face.

"No, not really. I mean, I wouldn't recognize the man that pulled me out if I saw him again tomorrow. I mean, your uncle could very well be him. I don't know, do I?"

Abdulla grinned.

"Thank you," he said, and then spoke rapidly to Hussein, who grabbed my hand and shook it so violently it hurt. They left, chattering amongst themselves. I thought about Abdulla's accusation, and felt a little guilty. Still, it was just a trick, and it hadn't done any harm. In fact it had done some good, I thought.

125

12

In April, on Fools' Day, the windows of the sky were opened wide.

Cass woke to the sound of rain on the roof and water rushing through the streets and found the land in biblical flood.

The shipyards of Aden, where the dhows grew from piles of woodshavings like leviathans from brown foam, are said to be the birthplace of Noah's Ark. On the slopes of Crater, forested almost within living memory, Noah and his sons once felled cypress trees with stone axes, hewed the trunks with flint scrapers, burned them into flat ribs, steamed the ribs into shape, and pegged and strapped them together, for there could have been no metal tools or nails in the beginning of the world. The wooden skeleton was covered in reeds and then painted with pitch. What a mighty task that must have been, to build a giant canoe with nothing but hands and stone! Japheth, Ham and Shem, working alongside their father, believing him mad yet willing to sacrifice five, ten, fifteen years perhaps, in order to satiate the old man's obsession.

And the shadowy nameless wives, who did most of the hard heavy work, carrying logs, boiling urns of pitch over slow fires, burning their hands, blistering their backs under the hot sun. The long-suffering wives who cooked and sewed and fetched the water, as well as harvesting and carrying huge bundles of reeds, dragging thick beams of timber over rough ground, while the men did the interesting work of putting the ark together.

Finally the ark was finished and, wonder of wonders, the rains came in torrents, turning the streams to rivers, the rivers to lakes, the lakes to seas. Next to witness their friends and relations desperately clawing their way up the muddy slopes towards the ark, their homes gone, their livestock drowned, only to be swept away too before reaching the safety of the sleek, shapely craft. Noah, standing on the bridge making ready to cast off, looking on helplessly as his neighbours bobbed away on the flood, terror in their eyes, to certain death.

Then to battle against the never-ending darkness and storms while enclosed with lions and tigers, walking below decks, watching the shadows for prowling carnivores, keeping the cats from the mice, the dogs from the cats, the panthers from the dogs. Eking out the feed, the grain, the hay, the flesh-food for the meat-eaters. A nightmare of logistics. On top of that, the terrible loneliness on realizing the rest of the human race had gone, watching the bodies float by in their thousands, keeping the scavengers, the ravens and vultures, from the bloated dead, witnessing the feasting of the sharks.

And the boredom, the ugly boredom, gnawing at their souls. Weeks, months, years, with nothing to do but stare at rain-filled skies or muddy swirling waters.

Up on the bridge, one of Noah's sons, trying to navigate by stars that had not yet been given names, attempting to sail a ship without ever having learned sea lore or a mariner's skills, looking, hoping for land where there was only water. What a hell the living had then.

And this, the reward for goodness.

Almost three inches of rain fell on Aden on the morning of April Fools' Day in 1967 and water spilled and gushed down the slopes of Jebel Shamsan. Transient streams appeared and disappeared within the hour, carving new gullies, forming waterfalls, bursting through natural dams. Vines of water twisted through former arid chimneys, turned into muddy rivers along streets, swirled around corners of buildings.

Silt poured down from the hillsides to cover houses; shanty dwellings were swept away; vehicles were immobilized. They were not ready for it: there had been no rain for six years. There were cascades from every ledge on the volcano, and goat tracks became the beds of streams. It was difficult to see where the ocean ended and the land began. The ground was hard-baked, impervious. There was no drainage for the deluge. Men waded through the floodwaters, up to their necks, simply to cross a road.

"Are you two coming to breakfast?" Cass asked Del and Blue 16.

They stood staring over the balcony rail, contemplating the mayhem before them. There was a river between their block and the cookhouse below. No doubt they would be called out shortly, to assist with all the work that needed to be done.

"No chance," said Del. "Quicker to get the fishing-rods out."

Down below a Land-Rover attempted to enter the waters from high ground and immediately stalled. After a few moments its occupants abandoned it, as the wheels sank in the softened sand and the vehicle gradually disappeared beneath the surface of the lake.

Later, a motorboat cruised over the football pitches, sending a wash through the barely visible goal posts. There was a lone man at the helm. He was dressed in white shorts and shirt.

"Look at that," said Del, "the ghost of Donald Campbell."

Earlier in the year a man had tried to break records on Coniston Water and had broken his neck instead. Three other men trying to set a different kind of record, Gus Grissom, Ed White and Roger Chaffee, had died in a fire. The wages of risk, of trying to break through the barriers of fire and water, are sometimes death. Noble ways to die. Cass thought about that. Was he prepared to die nobly for his country? What country? England? Aden? For whom? The politicians and the generals? For what? So that an oligarchy of nobles could be left in charge? Did any of that make sense? Would his death advance the quality of life one fraction, for anyone at all? No, was the answer. No, no, no. Everyone was afraid of that word. It brought the wrath of queen and country down on your head. The heavy brass gathered to crush you to a pulp. The mighty machine was turned against you.

No? Court martial. Disgrace. Dishonour.

Better to say *yes* and hope you lived through the experience.

Cass picked up his binoculars and looked through them at the man in the boat.

"Oi!" said Blue 16. "They're for lookin' at birds, not blokes."

"Not Donald Campbell's ghost," said Cass. "It's Billy Jiggs. I bet he's pinched it from the jetty. Silly bugger. He'll end up in the glasshouse."

"If they can catch him," laughed Del.

Shortly afterwards a sergeant arrived and told them they had to report to the guardroom, to help start clearing up the mess.

"I knew it," groaned Blue 16.

That was on Saturday.

On Sunday, the next day, the UN Mission arrived and promptly disappeared into a building. They were hardly seen again, except to criticize, and left in anger a few days later, having accomplished very little. Amnesty International, too, had not been without their prejudices when they visited Aden. Organizations with good intentions also have their bigots: to err on the side of righteousness is still injustice.

The General Strike began that Sunday, and while Cass, Del and Blue 16 were at work clearing up the flood damage there were twelve terrorist attacks taking place. NLF and FLOSY terrorists threw three grenades, loosed two Energa rockets and fired on security forces with small arms on seven different occasions. This set the pace for the week, at the end of which *The Dhow* produced the following:

129

THE SCOREBOARD

	Incidents
Grenades	112
Small Arms Fire at Security Forces	139
Mines	3
Mortars	10
Rockets	
Blindicide	1
Energa	12
Total	277

"Scoreboard? Anyone would think it was a bleeding darts match," grumbled Del, throwing the newspaper aside. Like all the others on the balcony, he wore only a folded towel around his loins. He shifted it down a little, to reveal a waistline raw with prickly heat. Producing a tin of talcum powder he sprinkled some on the rash, which Cass knew must have been driving his friend crazy with itching. They all had some minor local complaint. Blue 16 had an impetigo sore on his lip. Cass suffered from sunburn. He had spent his childhood in this land and still he burned while others browned.

"All I know is," said Blue 16, lying like a limp rag on his bed, "that bits of me are falling off. My whole body aches. I don't care if I never see another drop of rain in my whole life." The only part of him that moved was his right wrist when flicking his swatter. Since the rains there had been a plague of flies. They were everywhere, in thick black clouds. It was difficult to breathe without taking one or two down. First Noah, then Moses.

"I'm the only happy one of the trio," said Cass, staring at the strange green world below the balcony. "I've got a date."

"WHAT?" cried his two friends in unison.

*   *   *

Cass had been consigned to the buildings near the maidan, where the floodwaters had created some of the worst damage. Most of the time he worked alongside others, clearing the lower flats of a six-storey block of married quarters. The rooms were now occupied by senior non-commissioned officers, who mucked in with the rest of the lads in digging ditches and drains to allow the water to flow away.

Towards the end of the day, a sergeant came to Cass and said, "Corp, take a couple of men and go over and help the nurses with their place. They've got rid of most of the floodwater, but there's a lot of mopping up to do."

Cass signalled to two airmen, and the three of them crossed the flooded maidan to the nurses' quarters, a long single-storey shack separated into a row of twenty individual rooms. It was one of those buildings that he and Blue normally viewed from afar, through a pair of binoculars, and when he finally set foot inside he felt a pang of guilt ripple through his conscience.

There were about six nurses there, working with mops and pails, and carrying items from one room to the next. The rest of them were probably on duty, at the hospital.

"You two help the lasses at the other end," he told the airmen. "I'll start down here."

The first two rooms had people working in them, but the third was locked.

"Anyone got the key to next door?" he asked a dark-haired woman, trying not to notice that she had her skirt tucked up into her knickers, and was showing more female leg than he had dreamed of since leaving England.

The broad-faced nurse smiled, obviously aware of his discomfort, but she didn't capitalize on it. He was grateful for that. He hated being teased and was easily embarrassed into blushing.

"Suzie and Judith's room? I can let you in. They're at work at the moment. Should be back soon."

The woman spoke in efficient clipped sentences: presumably the style she used with patients.

She unlocked the door for him with a bunch of master keys and he entered the room to find it still swimming in about two inches of water. There were two single beds, two small wardrobes, and a chest of drawers. On the floor he found two sodden books, an opened packet of sanitary towels, some disintegrating cigarettes, several items of clothing, three pairs of shoes, a tennis racquet, and a plastic bag with some letters inside.

The letters were fairly dry so he put them in the top drawer of the chest and used the plastic bag as a dirty-washing bag. Opening the window he laid the books out on the sill, to dry in the sun. They would bulge out of shape, of course, but it was worth trying to save them. He was not sure what to do with the sanitary towels, whether to throw them away, or put them somewhere high. The nurses' quarters had communal washrooms, so he couldn't put them in a medicine cabinet. In the end he stuck them on a shelf above the bed.

He was busy with a mop and bucket when he sensed someone in the doorway and turned to see a small pretty woman in nurse's uniform standing there.

"Hey," she said brightly, "you've done well. This place was a mess when I left this morning."

"It's still a bit of a mess," Cass said apologetically.

"Not as bad as it was. Here," she kicked off her shoes into the corridor, "let me help. It's my room after all."

He said, "What about your roommate?"

The nurse laughed.

"Judith? She won't be back until gone midnight. She's courting one of the doctors."

"You must be Suzie then?"

She looked at him quizzically.

"Yes, but I prefer *Susanne*'."

Immediately he felt himself going hot, and he became flustered.

"I'm sorry. I wasn't . . . the other nurse, she called you 'Suzie'."

Susanne smiled.

"That's okay. I'm not fanatical about it. I'm just telling you what I prefer. Come on, let's finish this place and then you can take me somewhere for a drink. I'm just about ready for lager."

He smiled at her, bent to his task, and only after a few seconds did it register what she had said. A flush of excitement went through him. *She wanted him to take her for a drink!* He looked up at her again, but she had her back to him, and was wiping down the walls with a cloth. She had a slim athletic figure, not overly endowed with curves, but neat and trim.

"Soon dry out," she said over her shoulder, as if she were aware of his eyes on her. "That's one thing about this place, no lack of heat."

He cleared his throat and said, "That book I've put on the windowsill – Carson McCullers' *Ballad of the Sad Café*. Is it yours, or what's-her-name, Judith's?"

"Mine, why? Is it ruined?"

He was happy. McCullers was one of *his* writers.

'No, I mean, yes it probably is, but I asked because it's one of my favourites. I think Carson McCullers is brilliant. Have you read *Reflections in a Golden Eye*?"

"Yes, she is good, isn't she?"

He asked, "Do you like American novelists?"

She turned and flashed him a brilliant smile.

"I just like good books, and you do too, don't you?"

"How did you know?"

"I can tell."

Suddenly she saw the box of sanitary towels, which was dripping water on to the sheets. "Oh, damn . . . " she muttered. She snatched them from the shelf and tossed them to him. He caught them two-handed, the way he would catch a cricket ball.

"You didn't need to rescue those, they'll be useless anyway. It was sweet of you to try. Throw them in the bin outside, will you?"

He did as he was asked, discovering the eunuch crouched down within himself. Like most unmarried men he felt meek in the world of the female. Everything was pastel-coloured and

133

smelled of perfume: it was an alien environment where strange customs were enacted and the laws of nature were quite different. It was best to do as he was told, without question. He took the box out to the dustbin and quickly dropped it inside, slamming the lid down, worried that one of the airmen might catch him at this contemptible errand, in the way that a high-caste Indian might be concerned about being found doing the work of untouchables.

Since the rains, Aden had bloomed. Seeds, dormant since all in the Garden of Eden had withered and died way back in Genesis, had sprung to life. A light green fuzz, softer than the down on the cheek of a youth, hid the sand and in some cases the rock beneath. Cass remembered his tomatoes and cod-liver oil trees, as a young boy: how they appeared almost overnight from nothing.

"Just add water," Cass mused. "Look at that beautiful green world out there: a flourishing garden."

"Wait a minute," said Del, "you don't get out of it that easily. Never mind the poetics for a minute. You can dream about your verse and stuff later. What's this about a date?"

"Oh, that?" said Cass.

"Yeah, *that*," cried Blue 16.

"One of the nurses, up at the hospital. Susanne McNiece – sorry, not McNiece – *Williams*. A Welsh girl. I think she likes me. I helped her clear out her room. It was under several inches of water."

Del's features creased with a smile.

"You jammy bugger. You little jammy bugger!" He punched Cass on the arm, and Cass grinned.

"Aren't I though? She's nice. Nice little round face and big eyes. Bette Davis eyes."

"Yeah, big *eyes*," growled Blue 16.

"Enough of that," said Cass. "I told you, she's a nice girl."

"Nice big eyes," growled Blue 16, and Cass threw a Georgette Heyer novel at him.

"It's like *Cotillion*, Blue – strictly for gentlemen only."

They watched him getting dressed for his date that night, fussed over him like two older married sisters over the single youngest. It was the first time he had worn a tie since arriving in Aden. When he was ready he gave them a twirl.

"What do you reckon?" he said.

"Be in by ten, or there'll be trouble," said Del.

"Yes Mamma."

He left them to their beers and walked down the hill to the women's barracks at the bottom. The stars were out: a rash of white. He kicked his way through the green fuzz. Small delicate red flowers were beginning to appear like tiny drops of blood. Cass wondered how long they would last without water. It amazed him how quickly a landscape could be transformed, however superficially, from a dust bowl to pleasant walks and green hills. Perhaps some of those small plants were oaks, cedars, elms? If they continued to get moisture maybe the forests would return, and deer and foxes and raptors?

More likely it would all wither and die, like everything else in Aden.

She was waiting for him, by the gate, which surprised him. In England he had always been expected to wait for them, sometimes for ever when they stood him up. He had always had trouble with girls. The fact was, he was wrong for the kind of women he used to meet at dance-halls like the Kursaal at Southend, or the Samson and Hercules in Norwich. Those kind of girls liked muscle, stylish clothes and wicked wit, though not too much brain power. They liked their men to go bad on them occasionally, hitting other men, or touching other women, though they screamed blue murder at both. They were suspicious of men who enjoyed poetry and literature. They preferred the cinema to the theatre, and if they ever went to the latter it was to see a farce, not *Macbeth*. Cass made mistakes, like trying to lend them

135

copies of *The Iliad*, instead of thrillers. Even those men who were like Cass pretended they weren't. There were women in the world for Cass, but he didn't go to places where he might meet them, and if he had, he would have been serving the drinks.

Yet, she was waiting for him. Not only that, she was not like any woman he had met since Heather. Susanne had been well educated, though she seemed to kick against it. Why *him* in the first place? There were thousands of men, all clamouring for a woman, and here was one willing to go out with a man too shy to say hello, let alone ask for a date. It was she who had done the asking.

Now they were meeting, however, the roles had reversed again. It was she who looked vulnerable under the security lights, like a small creature caught in the glare of hunters' lamps. His shyness was behind him, now that he did not have to ask and stand waiting to be rejected.

"Those your pals up there?" she said.

Cass turned and looked over his shoulder. Del and Blue 16 were jumping up and down on their beds, waving their arms. When they saw he was looking, they turned away and whipped off their towels, baring their backsides.

"Yes," he said, turning back again, "I'm sorry."

"You must be a lapsed Catholic," she said.

"Why?"

"Oh, they're always apologizing for something they can't do anything about. Like the weather. *Sorry you had to come here in the rain today*. Things like that. It has to do with guilt."

"Are you a lapsed Catholic?"

"Funny you should ask me that." She smiled. "I was raised in a convent. The nuns were like blackbirds, pecking at me all the time I was there. I think it turned me against religion."

"A Welsh Roman Catholic?"

"They do have them, you know. We're not all chapel."

"I'm an Anglican," he said.

"Good for you. I'm not anything, now. At least I say that, but

136

there are times when I'm worried – you know – worried about what will happen to me, later. Hellfire, I suppose. I committed a mortal sin once. Swallowed some toothpaste while I was cleaning my teeth and then told the priest at mass that I hadn't eaten. So there you are, I was going into the flames anyway."

He laughed, but her eyes looked troubled.

"Sorry," he said.

"There you go again. You really should convert, you know, then immediately lapse. You're a born lapsed Catholic. You've missed your vocation. Where are you taking me?"

It was a silly question. There really was only one place to go and that was the Mermaid Club, the place Cass used to call the Lido when he was a boy.

"I thought we might go to the club."

She said, "Why don't we walk along Telegraph Beach?" and she slipped her arm around his waist. "We can look at the stars and tell each other nice things." They had already done a lot of talking, in her quarters, after the clearing up. Already they had established a rapport. There was a certain harmony which he could feel and they both knew there was something more than ordinary between them.

He didn't dare look up at the boys as they strolled down the road, split and crumbling after the flood. He knew they would be watching, and saying things like, "Put her arm round him. Moves in the fast lane, don't she? Our Cass is goin' to get eaten alive if he ain't careful."

They did the usual thing: they talked about who and what they were, where they thought they were going. He told her he had been brought up in Aden and she expressed surprise and asked if it had changed a great deal. He told her it had.

"It must be horrible," she said, "seeing it like this. I'm trying to imagine what it would be like, going back to a Pembroke at war with itself."

"There's something strange going on in my head," he admitted. "It's as if this Aden has nothing to do with the Aden of my

137

boyhood. I can't seem to associate the two. I used to roam all over these rocks," he nodded up at the dark crags of Shamsan, "and now I can't go beyond the limits of Steamer Point without risking death. It all seems so unreal to me."

"What will you do when you've finished here?"

"Oh, I don't know. I've got some vague ideas about going to university, as a mature student. I've been gathering GCEs over the past few years, to get me in."

"What will you study?"

"English," he replied without hesitation, then he added, "I've never been much good at anything else."

"Give me a kiss," she said.

Immediately, he was thrown into confusion, but looked down into her eyes. It saved him. She was not so terrifying, after all. It was the *idea* of her that was frightening. He kissed her and they clung together for a long time, listening to the waves fall on the beach.

" *'A' thru the nicht I heard her hert, gang soundin' wi' my ain,'* " he quoted.

"What?" she asked softly.

"It's a poem by William Soutar. Two people meet in the night, they lie closely together, their hearts beat in time, then at dawn they have to part."

"How sad."

"Sadder than that, because as she slips away, so too do all his summer days, 'Like they had never been.' "

She clung to him more tightly and laughed a little.

"Oh, God, what are you trying to do to me? You've got me, you know. You don't need to quote poetry."

"I like poetry. I quote it because I like it." He paused, then added, "I like you too."

"I like you, Cass." She looked up at him. "What are we going to do about it?"

"I don't know. I'm not much good at this."

She took a deep breath.

"Well, let's take it slowly. Not rush it. You know I'm not a virgin, don't you? There have been two other men . . . "

"I don't want to . . . "

" . . . and I loved them both, very much. I'm not one of those who recants once it's all over. We've only just met. I like you a lot, Cass, but I want to be wooed for once. Can you woo me, Cass?"

He laughed. "It's probably the one thing I'm good at. I'm hopeless at sweeping people off their feet, but I'm pretty good at being romantic. Is that soft?"

"That's *lovely*. God, where have you *been*? I'm nearly twenty-four! Only one thing bothers me now. Where did you learn all this stuff?"

"All what?"

"How to turn a woman to jelly?"

He could feel her legs, warm against his, and they were indeed shaking. So were his own. He wanted to make love to her, there on the sand, but she had said she wanted to take things slowly. That was all right though, because he knew they would eventually make love. He was surprised how sure he was of that fact. He was going to tell her that the kind of girls he had been going out with were not turned to jelly by poetry, they were turned off. Instead he tried for a remark that might have impressed *them*.

"I've been around," he said.

"No," she said, seriously, "no you haven't. That's why it puzzles me. You've been in love before?"

"When I was a teenager."

"Oh," she laughed, "everyone had a teenage crush."

"It wasn't a crush, it was love," he said a little too sharply, then added, "really. She was fourteen when we parted and I felt as if I'd been torn in half. I don't know why I'm telling you this."

"Because you're falling in love again, for the first time since you were a boy?"

"Maybe." He smiled at her. "Maybe I am."

139

She held his face between her hands and looked deeply into his eyes.

"God, I'm jealous of her already," she said. "I'm not going to come up to scratch. Not against a memory like that."

"It's different," he said, pulling away. "One's like a poem that's already been written. The words are there and can't be changed."

"And the other?"

"We've got to write it, I suppose. But there's no point in comparing poems. Doesn't work like that."

"Good, I'm glad about that."

They held hands then and walked the short length of the beach. He felt happy. He motioned towards the ocean. It was dark and choppy, flicking up points on its waves, like the North Sea after a storm. If the night were not so balmy he could have been back home, on some beach in Cornwall, or Yorkshire.

"Some rain we had. I wrote home about it, telling Mum it was like Noah's flood."

"Yes, I suppose it was," she said in a guarded tone. "Does the Bible interest you?"

"Oh, yes. All religions interest me. I find the stories fascinating – the myths and things. I love the story of Noah, it's so impractical. You've got to *feel* it, emotionally, or it doesn't work. I mean, listen to this for a start: a boat three hundred cubits, by fifty cubits, by thirty cubits. A cubit is from knuckles to elbow. You know what that makes the ark look like?"

"No," she smiled, "what does that make the ark look like?"

"No, seriously, it makes it look like a war canoe, about the length of a football pitch. You scale it down in your mind – a hundred and thirty inches long, by twenty inches wide. Long and narrow, like a giant canoe. Then ... "

"*Then*," she repeated dramatically, her eyes shining.

"You're not taking this seriously. Then *twelve inches deep*. That makes it look like a Dyak war canoe ... "

"Only, as long as a football pitch."

"Yes, with a roof on top."

She said, "How do you know all this?"

"I made one, out of paper, the other day."

"*You made a Noah's Ark?*"

"Scaled-down model, just to see what it looked like."

She hugged him.

"Boy, I wish I'd had you teaching me, instead of those nuns. I might have enjoyed it. Have you ever thought of teaching? I mean that seriously."

"No, the kids wouldn't respect me. I'm too close to childhood myself. Much closer than I am to being an adult."

He walked her back to her quarters, explaining on the way that perhaps Noah's Ark wasn't so far-fetched, that maybe Noah represented all the men at the time who managed to get to their canoes with their wives and children and livestock, as the Ice Age came to an end and there were floods in every part of the land.

They arranged to meet the next day. When he got back to the billet he received the usual barrage of asinine remarks, about whether he had, or hadn't, and if he had, did he get sand in it, doing it on the beach.

A thought suddenly came to him.

"You bastards. You were watching us through binoculars."

"Only *some* of the time," grinned Del.

"Well, most of the time, really," smiled Blue 16, "I mean, what other entertainment have we got?"

Shortly afterwards, a grenade was thrown at one of the road-blocks not far away and the sound reverberated around the walls of Crater, making heads sing and hearts falter. The local forces radio was playing "Homeward Bound" by Simon and Garfunkel, a record that was requested endlessly by the troops. Earlier, someone had put in a request using only the nicknames of the sender and proposed receiver. Something like, "Could you play this for Duddy, from Trix?" It wasn't until halfway through the record that the DJ was informed by an irate orderly officer that

141

Duddy was a soldier who was in jail awaiting execution for the murder of an Arab waiter. The DJ stopped the record and stuttered an apology.

The record requested was Tom Jones's "Green, Green Grass of Home".

Somebody had a sick sense of humour.

13

There was a rumour amongst the schoolchildren that there was to be a public hanging in Crater. A double hanging. A woman and her lover, so the rumour went, had murdered the woman's husband. Though I had no idea how the murder was supposed to have been carried out, I had images in my mind which had similarities with the assassination of Julius Caesar: a man and woman waiting in the darkness with drawn *jambias*; the unsuspecting husband returning after a hard day at work; the killers then falling on him, stabbing him repeatedly; the husband dropping to the ground with an exclamation that might go down in the history books. We were, of course, studying Shakespeare's *Julius Caesar* in class at the time. Had we been doing *Macbeth* the scene might have consisted of two men duelling to the death, the husband losing to the lover.

Dix said he could remember public hangings in Bulawayo, though he had never been to one.

"We ought to get to see it," said Dix, "if we can. I mean, it's hist'ry isn't it? We might not ever get to see another one."

I was a bit dubious about permission.

"Our parents'll never let us go."

"So we don't tell them. What we do is we get some binoculars and climb up to the edge of Crater, then we can look down and see it from there. We pretend we're going to school, see. Then we walk along the beach to Crater. Easy."

He flexed his muscular body, a sure sign that he was feeling either excited or nervous. Dix had a morbid fascination with

143

injury and death. He once ran from the swimming pool, to where I was happily messing around in sandpools on the beach, and dragged me back to see a man who had fallen from the top diving board on to the concrete parapet that ran around the edge of the pool. The man had injured his spine: probably broken it. He was big and husky-looking but he lay on the tiles pale and withdrawn, looking up at the ring of faces through the frightened eyes of a gazelle. Someone put a rolled-up T-shirt under his head, but the general murmur was, "Don't move him, mustn't move him."

Dix couldn't take his gaze off the injured man and finally blurted, "Does it hurt much, mister?"

The man turned his terrified eyes on Dix's face, but he made no reply. Several of the onlookers shushed Dix with shocked voices. I tapped him on the ankle with my foot, indicating that we should get out of the way, but he took no notice. Someone else's pain was like a magnet to him. I was never sure whether he was horrified by the thought that it might be him lying there limp and broken, or whether he was interested in a detached way. He seemed as intrigued with pain as he was with the comic-book version of horror stories like Edgar Allan Poe's "The Tell-tale Heart". I realized afterwards that he had only fetched me to the scene in order that he could talk about it later.

"Did you see his face? Must've paralysed him or something, 'cos he didn't yell much, did he? Do you think he was paralysed, maybe from the neck down?"

I told him I didn't know and didn't care, which he said surprised him, but made no further comment.

Also, at the time of the murder of the beggar, outside the gates of Khormaksar, Dix had wanted to see the body. He was actually angry with himself for not being around when it happened.

"If we hadn't gone camping, we'd have been the ones to find him first," he said. "I mean, it's us that's usually up first on a weekend. All the grown-ups sleep in. I would've come over to get you for church and we would've seen the corpse of him, drooped all over that broken bed. Don't suppose we'll get to see anything like that again."

I surprised him again by saying I was pretty glad we hadn't been at home. My lack of interest in morbid subjects was a great disappointment to him, I know.

When the rumours of a public hanging were humming through the school, Dix was eager to verify them.

"Supposed to be Friday morning. We'll have to dodge school," he said that evening, as we sat on Heather's veranda. Heather was not pleased with us. She was trying to write a letter home, sitting in a rattan chair with the pad on her knees. It was an awkward position which had her bending almost double when she was actually putting pen to paper. I was more interested in learning the name of the recipient, thinking it might be one of her old flames, probably a Highland laddie with red hair and blue eyes, the boy who really had her heart, back in the Cairngorms, and to whom she would *return* once her colonial days were over. Jealousy had fashioned a cage around me and was taunting me through the bars.

"Listen you two, I think this is silly," she said in that voice which transformed her from a girl into a woman on occasions like these. "Why on earth do you want to go and watch someone being hanged? It's horrible."

"Well, we don't actually know if it's on yet," said Dix, as if this explained our reasons for wanting to go. "That's what we've got to find out. We can't ask the parents, they'll get suspicious and forbid us to go anywhere near it."

"Quite right too," said Heather. "Honestly, I sometimes wonder what goes on in your heads. You two can be a mystery to me."

I wanted to say to her that I thought the scheme was dopey too, but that would have been taken by Dix as a terrible betrayal and he probably wouldn't have spoken to me for a long while afterwards. If something was important to him, he naturally assumed it was important to me too. I didn't want to hurt him that badly. Sometimes I wanted to kill him, when he was stacking

145

up points with Heather, telling her how much he liked classical music, but that was different. During those times if we could have fought to the death in single combat, we would have done, but one of us would have died respecting the other, seeing his point of view. There was honour in battling over the attention of a lady. The hanging business was a question of loyalty. He would never have understood if I went against him on this matter.

Heather jumped up and put her pad on the chair.

"Well, I'm fed up with talking about it. I'm going for a walk around the houses. Is anyone coming with me?"

We were both meant to leap to our feet shouting, "Me! Me!"

Dix was on his feet in a flash, but I stayed where I was.

"I'm feeling a bit tired," I said. "I did a lot of swimming today. I think I'll stay here a bit."

Heather looked at me in amazement and Dix frowned. He was my best friend. He knew me inside out. Dix realized there was something going on.

"What, just sit here?" he said.

I yawned. "Just for a bit. I might catch you up later."

Heather came to her senses.

"Suit yourself, chum. We'll be visiting Bags."

Then she took Dix's arm and led him off. I watched them go, very annoyed with both of them. They knew that touching was not allowed. She was only doing it to make me jump to my feet and come racing after her. Well, I wasn't going to do it. Not for a few moments anyway.

As soon as they were out of sight, I did indeed jump to my feet. I grabbed the notepad which Heather had left face down on her seat and quickly turned to the first page. It read: *Dear Auntie Jean.* My heart was immediately several pounds lighter. There was no swashbuckling son of Rob Roy in her life: only an aunt who went by the name of Jean. A good Scottish name. My head began to spin with poems. *"That nane can be sae dear to me as my sweet lovely Jean!"* Burns. *"I'm wearing awa' Jean, like snaw, when it's thaw, Jean, I'm wearing awa', to the land o' the Leal."* Lady

146

Nairne. I clutched the chair for support, feeling giddy, then shook my head clear. Placing the pad in exactly the same position as I had found it, I ran off in search of my two friends.

When I turned the corner, they were nowhere in sight. I ran all the way to Bags's house, without bumping into them. The darkness had fallen and by the time I reached my destination, veranda lights were on and living rooms were lit. Even from twenty yards away I could see Bags and his family, sitting down to a meal.

Somehow, Dix and Heather had given me the slip.

I ran all the way back to the house, to find them sitting on the veranda as if they had never moved. Heather was back writing letters again. Dix was bouncing a tennis ball against the end wall, softly, so as not to disturb anyone in the house. He gave me an infuriating grin.

"Where *have* you been?" said Heather, looking up from the letter.

"Oh, just out for a stroll."

"I thought you were tired?"

"Changed my mind," I said.

"Really," she said, sweetly, "and where did you go?"

"Oh, I wanted to be alone for a bit. To think. I went in the opposite direction to you two. I didn't want to be disturbed."

"Is that a fact?" she said, in a broad Scottish accent. When she did that it meant she had got your measure.

"No, really," I said.

"Really," she repeated. Then to Dix she said, "I don't want to leave you out of this, so it's better you know too. I'm writing a letter to my auntie – Auntie Jean."

Dix looked puzzled.

"What do I want to know that for?"

"I think Cass wanted to know."

Somehow she knew I had looked at her letter. I didn't know what to do. I know I blushed and said hotly, "No I didn't."

I felt sick, ghastly. I was so embarrassed. I was also terrified

147

that I had committed a cardinal sin and would never be forgiven. I expected her next words to be, "How *could* you, Cass? It's easy to see what kind of background *you* come from. In our society we do not read each other's private mail without being given leave to do so. It's terribly rude, a gross breach of etiquette, manners, breeding and all that's decent. Get out of my sight. I never want to see you again, and please don't try to speak to me because if you do, I shall have to ignore you."

How had she found out that I had invaded her privacy? Was it the position of the writing pad? Maybe Brian had seen me and had snitched on me? Or perhaps it was just intuition? The fear freezing my good sense, I decided to bluff it out.

"I don't know what you're talking about, I'm sorry."

She laughed at me then. It was a gentle affectionate laugh that took me by surprise. I almost reeled, as if from a slap.

"Oh Cass, you're so transparent. I think it's why I like you so much. I'm not angry, you know. I'm flattered to think that it should bother you, that you care. Now we'll say no more about it," and she bent her head to her task again.

Dix looked at me and frowned. We both knew that I had just scored a vast number of points, but neither of us were sure how I'd done it. If we had, we'd have tried it again some time.

When the time came for us to leave, Heather reached forward and with a licked finger smoothed down one of my eyebrows.

"You've got lovely black eyebrows," she said, "you could be an Italian, or something Latin anyway."

The skin on her fingers was like satin. Her touch sent a shiver of delight through me. I wanted at that moment to hug her and tell her I wished to be with her for ever.

"It's gypsy," I blurted, wanting her to see that I could be honest as well as deceitful, even though she hadn't minded about my sneaky behaviour. "It's only gypsy."

"Gypsies are very romantic," she said.

Dix was standing by, bathing in thunder.

148

Heather said, "So I won't see you two at school tomorrow? You're both going to dodge off?"

"Well *I* am," said Dix, still glaring at both of us.

"Then I'll see you tomorrow evening," she said.

The next morning I feigned a headache and told my mother I was too ill to go to school. My brothers left for school and my dad went off to work. Shortly afterwards my mother came up to see me and asked if she should stay home. I hadn't thought of that and was horrified, not only because I would not be able to get out of the house but because she might get into trouble from her boss, for failing to turn up for work. We had no phone in those days.

"No, you go in," I said. "I'll be all right. I've taken some aspirins."

So, to my relief, off she went.

Dix arrived at nine. He had done nothing except leave the house. His parents thought he was at school. That was pretty dangerous, if Mrs Gower decided to check on his absence. However, I had no time to remonstrate with him because the hanging was supposed to be at ten. We ran from the house, through the back gate, and down to Khormaksar beach. Once on the sands, we trotted along to where the wall of Crater rose from the end of the bay. There we started to climb the rugged exterior of the cone, using the goat tracks as paths.

When we reached the rim, we climbed a low wall, the remnant of a Turkish or Portuguese fortification. There was a *sangar* built into the cliff-face near by – a sort of camouflaged hideout for riflemen – and we tucked ourselves in there, so as not to be seen from the beach or from below, in the streets of Crater.

The houses below us were like hundreds of sugar cubes, scattered over the bottom of a giant black basin. Through these cubes, some of which had melted into their neighbours, ran strips of liquorice. Occasionally, mostly on the junctions, mosques

149

appeared looking like birthday cakes, their minarets candles waiting to be lit.

We could see the colourful *suq*, the bolts of sari fabric unravelled and laid out to attract the tourists. We could see car parks, and schools, and public buildings. What we could not see, not completely, was the football pitch where the hanging was supposed to take place. The buildings were at such an angle around this area as to block our view. All we could see was one corner of the ground, where a great crowd of people had gathered and were huddled together. We talked about moving to another spot, but the climbs on both sides were difficult. We were stuck in a deep saddle and to move either way would have meant going down and starting up again in a different area.

"Damn," said Dix, looking through the battered pair of brass naval binoculars he had been given as a present by his uncle, "can't see the gallows."

Gallows? The instrument of death now had a name in my head. Personally I was glad we couldn't see the *gallows*. I had nightmares about such wooden structures as gallows or scaffolds. In those bad dreams I was always an innocent, caught up in circumstances not of my making, climbing the wooden steps one by one towards the rope.

We sat in the *sangar* and sweated. As usual, the day was oven-hot, and we were fully exposed to it. You couldn't touch the rocks without burning your hand. We had already tired of experiments such as frying eggs on stones. We knew the air was hot, the sand was hot, the rock was hot. If you spat on a flat surface, it sizzled.

So we tried to keep in the shade, though the air became stifling inside the *sangar*. We stared at our watches and the time crept by agonizingly slowly. I watched some ants carry large grains of dust from one place to another. They toiled in the sun, oblivious of its heat. These ants were porters and warehouse workers, builders and creators, unlike the ants at home, who seemed to do nothing but prepare for war, attack and slaughter their

150

enemies, then retire to take care of their wounded. The house ants made a living out of death. These hillside ants seemed to be getting on with building and storing things.

Ten o'clock finally arrived, but nothing happened down below. We could see all the people gathered on the corner that was visible to us, but nothing seemed to be going on. I tried to gauge whether there was an air of expectancy about the crowd, but we were too far away to hear any buzz or catch an atmosphere of excitement. There were shouts, but incomprehensible to us. Then, a quarter of an hour later, a great cheer went up. Hats were thrown in the air and arms were waved. Something momentous had taken place out of our line of vision. Dix had a good look through the binoculars. Then I had a go. The people below seemed agitated now. Excited. They milled around like ants. Then ten minutes later there was another loud cheer.

Twelve minutes after that they broke up and began drifting in all directions, mostly in small knots.

Dix nodded in satisfaction.

"That's it then."

"What?" I said.

"They've been hung," he said, grimly, still staring through the binoculars.

"Can you see them?" I asked, fearfully, thinking he was watching the bodies being carted away.

"No, I can't *see* 'em, but they must've been dropped – that's what the cheer was, obviously. Two cheers, one for each."

I had my doubts.

"Are you sure?" I said.

He let the binoculars go, the strap around his neck preventing them from falling two or three hundred feet down the cliff.

" 'Course I'm sure," he said, confidently.

We climbed down the outside slope of Crater and walked home along Khormaksar beach. Dix said we ought to look at the spot where the turtles' eggs were, to see if they had hatched. We had of course forgotten all about them until that moment. We dug in the sand, in a few places, but found nothing, not even the remnants of leathery shells.

That evening on Heather's veranda, we told her we had seen the hanging, that it was an awful experience and we would rather not say any more about it. She nodded, gravely. She then asked us what excuses we would have the following morning, when Mrs Gower asked us to account for our absence. Even the other pupils thought it highly suspicious that both of us were missing on the same day, since everyone knew we were inseparable. I told her I would have a note from my mother, saying I was ill. Dix took off his glasses, polished them on his handkerchief, and then looking at the spectacles as if they had given him the idea, announced that he had no real excuse but was going to say he had visited the opticians.

"What happens if she asks for proof?" said Heather.

"She'll just have to take my word for it, won't she?" said Dix. "If it goes any further than that, I'll get whacked I suppose."

He said it with just the right amount of aplomb. Heather stared at him in admiration. I felt my recently gained points running away like grains of sand in an hourglass.

The rest of the evening went pleasantly enough, though I had for a few moments to stand watching Dix and Heather reading an article together, about a concert they said I wouldn't be interested in. Their faces were too close to each other for the scene not to bother me. Then Dix and I walked home. I went to bed, wondering whether I would have a nightmare, though as I lay there waiting for sleep, I wasn't sure we had overseen a hanging. I wasn't sure at all. Crowds gather for many reasons: politics, sports, excursions. Many reasons. The hanging was supposed to have taken place on a football pitch blocked from our direct line of sight by buildings. Thinking over the morning's events, I wasn't *really* sure whether I had witnessed a crowd at a hanging, or spectators at a football match. Each cheer might have been for the drop of a trapdoor, or for the scoring of a goal. I don't suppose I'll ever know, now.

14

When the desert starts at your doorstep it is difficult to accept it as a threat. It's like living on the seafront of some British holiday resort. There's the ocean, just a few yards away, and it stretches to beyond the limits of your imagination. It's a place full of terrible storms, strange creatures, dangerous currents, cold water that can freeze your muscles to a standstill. So what? You don't plan to set sail in a canoe and get lost in its millions of square miles of nothingness. It might be on your doorstep but the probability is you will never have to actually venture into its watery wastes. It's there, and that's that. No further thought is necessary. So the threatening nature of the ocean, or the desert, can be ignored. Just as you never need jump over the edge of a high cliff, neither do you need to go out into emptiness.

It was a fact, though, that if I had a brainstorm one day and stepped out of my back door and started walking north-east, the chances are I would not hit an unnatural barrier until I came to the Gulf States, a thousand miles away. To get there I would have to cross the *Rub'al Khālī*, the empty quarter of the Arabian Desert. There would be mountains to cross, where the night airs would freeze my spittle solid. There would be hot sands that would vaporize that same spittle in seconds. There would be trackless wastes within which I could turn in circles until I disappeared into the dust, thinking that all the while I was walking in a straight line. Yet one step outside my back door and I was in that desert, the same sand beneath the sole of my foot that had been a dune in the middle of a furnace just weeks before, the grains having been blown for hundreds of miles by the hot winds, to land on my doorstep.

If I decided to walk directly north, instead, it would not be long before I would venture into the Radfan mountains where a savage tribe nicknamed the Red Wolves lived. The Red Wolves did not like their neighbours. The Red Wolves did not like their cousin tribes. The Red Wolves did not like each other very much. They killed where they saw offence, and if they were affronted by the mere proximity of relations and neighbours, even friends, they would certainly find the presence of a stranger offensive. It is doubtful whether one would get through the Radfan as a complete human being.

If I strolled north-east, I would find myself in al-Yemen, where Imam Ahmed ran his country like a medieval tyrant, shackling men, throwing them into dungeons and oubliettes, and beheading them. Where *jambias* were worn and drawn with the same frequency and intention as the Colts of nineteenth-century American gunslingers. Where an unclaimed white boy might be sold like a sack of millet to some misogynistic camel-driver.

These dangers at the bottom of my backyard were a fascination to me, rather than a horror. Rather like having fairies that one knew were there, even if one never saw them. The Arabian Desert was truly my backyard, for there were no fences around our house, only seemingly infinite sands. It is difficult not to imagine some spirit of the landscape out there, under those hard blue skies, which watches over strangers to its empty house.

My father had to go away on exercise upcountry. When he was gone, whether it was for days or weeks, sometimes months, Mother would fret the whole time and Duggy, Richie and I would find ourselves dodging flak which we had not precipitated. It wasn't that we considered this unfair – we knew the reasons for it – but we hated those times just the same. She would be nice to Dad, *extra* nice, right up until a few hours before he had to go, then there would be a flaming row. Said would find an excuse to visit his cousin and we boys would scatter to our bedrooms. When the storm, during which most of the thunder and lightning would come from Mum, with Dad merely dodging the bolts and trying unsuccessfully to soften the claps, when it had blown itself out, Mum would dissolve into tears and say she didn't mean it, she knew he had to go because the "bloody air force" said he had to, and there wasn't much he could do about it.

I suppose what Dad was doing at the time was a little dangerous, because he had to go out into the Hadhramaut desert, where there were warlike tribes, and play soldiers for a while. I don't expect he liked it himself very much, being just a simple farmer's boy who was in the air force because it was a job which earned money – though not a lot in those days – enough to keep his family. Dad was no military man who wanted to keep the world in order. Nor did he like guns very much, even though he was an armourer. He always said you didn't have to like people to be a Prime Minister. Guns and people, they were just things they paid you to manage, but not of especial interest in themselves. He was the first of the Carsons to join a force as a regular, though he used to joke that Kit Carson (no relation, of course), the famous Indian scout of the Wild West, had beaten him to it.

Both my grandfathers had been in the First World War; one of them had come out of it with only one leg, the other had spent the rest of his life – not a long one – with a shattered spine, confined to a wheelchair. I never knew Grandpa Willoughby, my mum's dad. He died before I was born, but Grandad Carson was a squarely-built taciturn man who clumped around on an artificial leg swearing at everything from sparrows to kings. He wasn't senile. He just didn't like anybody. Perhaps before the war he might have been a happy-go-lucky youth, but ever since I had been going to the tied cottage for my summer holidays he had been a "rotten old bugger" as my nanna put it. She couldn't stand him and she had been married to him for God knew how long, I never dared ask. The only person, who wasn't really a person at all, who would put up with Grandad Carson, was his dog, Grip – but then Grip didn't like anybody either. He would bite you soon as swallow his dinner.

Grip had a wall eye, all white with a tiny black pupil like a dead fly in the middle, and I was scared as hell of him. He spent most of his life either on the end of a chain in the yard or up beside Grandad on the tractor. When he was sitting on his old piece of sacking, up on the fender of the Massey-Ferguson, Grip became quite calm. He wouldn't bother with small boys on those occasions. His one good eye would be too busy sweeping the fields looking for wildlife. When a hare broke, or a stoat flowed out of the hedge, or rabbits exploded from a clump of corn, he went hurtling through the air regardless of what was going on around him, and gave chase. Several times I saw him miss certain death, on the curved spikes of reapers, or the honed discs of a harrow, by less than an inch. He cared nothing for threshing machines or harvesters. He scorned even my grandad's bellowing when there was a moving creature out in the fields somewhere, which he felt he deserved to crunch. Grip was a small stocky dog, dirty white with dusty black patches, of mixed parentage. He hated crows. He would have hated rooks too, except that they gathered in great numbers and were inclined to mob him on those rare occasions when he attacked, so he stopped hating them and concentrated on the more solitary members of that family.

Grip was one of those dogs you could never see as a puppy. He had not been born like other dogs, as one of a litter, but had emerged through a hole in the wall around hell, before it had been noticed and plugged again. Uncle Simon, my dad's brother who also worked as a farm labourer though not for the same landlord as Grandad, kept a shotgun next to him on his tractor. He said if he ever saw Grip out on his own he would separate the dog's body from its spirit. Nanna used to snort at this and say such was impossible, because the dog had no spirit.

156

Uncle Simon, like Uncle Nate on Mum's side of the family, had also been in the army, but both men had been conscripts. They had been in the army during the Second World War, but neither had left England. Uncle Simon said he would rather punch a farmer than shoot a German, so there wouldn't have been much point in sending him. Uncle Nate was a trawler fisherman at Harwich, like most of Mum's family, and he said he'd done his bit getting the British Army back from Dunkirk before they called him up. Along with the Felixstowe ferry, the cockleboats from Leigh-on-sea, and other East Anglian craft, he had rescued thousands of lads from the beaches of France.

There were four sisters on Mum's side, of which she was the eldest. They would have been fishwives had Other-nanna not found a salesman to follow to London after Grandpa died with the bullet that killed him still somewhere in his back. Instead they became cockney housewives. All except one, the youngest, who married a posh bloke from up North who manufactured cutlery, and she was looked on as gentry. There was no jealousy over this class-jump, since the remaining sisters wouldn't have been anything other than what they were for half the tea in China, so they said, and I believed them. They liked London, the pubs, the dog track, and everything that went with being what they were. Other-nanna had been a Harwich fishwife all her life, but took to being a cockney as if she'd been born sitting on one of Bow Bells. She and her friend Lil used to hold a perfectly understandable but shrill conversation shrieking at each other from three houses away, while they cooked the dinner for their respective spouses, neither leaving her own kitchen for a moment. When Other-nanna moved from Shepherd's Bush to a Victorian triple-storey house in Catford, Bill her second said she still tried to contact Lil from her kitchen window, but Other-nanna said that was a load of codswallop.

All the London side of the family was keen on greyhound racing. I remember being taken by Other-nanna and Bill to the Catford dog track, to see Barney Boy (trained by Bill at the

157

weekends) disgracing himself in front of thousands. Barney Boy had this trick of jumping the inner rail halfway round, sprinting across the oval, and springing back on to the track ahead of the other dogs. There he would wait for the mechanical hare and leap on it as it came around the bend. I thought this was pretty intelligent. I mean, all the other greyhounds were a bunch of dimwits for chasing a mock hare on a pole, while Barney Boy saw through this thin disguise and sought to intercept the quarry like some clever highwayman.

I thought the dog track was pretty exciting in those days, what with the ticktack men in their white gloves and their own cryptic semaphore, the seedy-looking weasel-faced men and dumpy women in make-up that had been chucked on in dollops. Everyone would be calm and talking amongst themselves in quiet voices. The runners would be displayed, one of them invariably crapping on the ground, which would have Bill nodding his head, saying, that's a winner for you, I always feel ten times better after a good crap myself, ha, ha, and Other-nanna apologizing for him to the people around us. Then, two minutes before the off, a bell would sound and the whole place would become electrified and people would be running backwards and forwards as if the stadium had hit an iceberg and was about to sink. Other-nanna and Bill always let me bet, too. When I was very young, about six or seven, I used to take a popgun to the races. As the winners were coming away from the tote or the bookies, counting their cash, big smiles on their faces, I used to say, "Stick 'em up, mister, your money or your liver!", and they would roar with laughter and say something like, "Oh dear, Jack Straw. Well, well. Have to be my money, won't it?" and slip me half-a-crown. It rarely failed. They were too full of themselves not to miss an opportunity to be generous and show how they remembered what it was like being a kid inventing games.

One of Dad's brothers was a jailbird, but they said it wasn't his fault because he was soft in the head. He must have been, because he used to rob pubs before they opened, so he only got

158

the change that was waiting in the till. Once, he tried to rob a bank but on his way out pushed the revolving doors the wrong way and got stuck.

Until my father was sent abroad the only members of our family to go overseas were the men. Some of them had seen France, but mostly from the viewpoint of the trenches, courtesy of HM travel agents. Apart from this limited experience, few had seen beyond the place where they had grown to adulthood. To try to explain to them about the desert, about Aden and Islam, and all the things that were influencing me day by day, would have been wasted time. It wasn't that they were incapable of understanding, but they had no real interest in exotic places. To them, the next Essex village, Suffolk fishing town or even London district, was exotic enough. They did things differently in Canewdon or South-wold or Hammersmith. They put different fertilizers on the crops. They hung net curtains up at their windows. They were a soft lot. They laid rugs on the lino to protect their feet against receiving a cold shock in the morning. They ploughed a different furrow.

Our letters home were confined to ordinary everyday news items, like what we had for breakfast on a Sunday, and how every day was a scorcher. This kind of information was not intimidating to those back in home village or city. It could be answered in kind. I have a complete week-by-week record, in my nanna's, other-nanna's and aunties' letters (the men never wrote, of course) of the British weather from 1953 to 1956. It was mostly cold and foggy in the winter and warmish to hot in the summer, with rain throughout.

I wrote lots of letters home while Dad was on exercise upcoun-try, to keep out of Mum's way a bit. When Dad came home she didn't settle down for a few days. It was as if he were still away. Then, gradually, things would get back to normal.

His experiences out in some desert wadi, surrounded by hos-tiles, seemed to leave Dad remarkably unaffected. It was as if he

159

had been to the circus. He'd seen some funny people, doing some funny things, and that was that. The desert? Well, it was just a lot of sand and rock. What he had looked forward to, at the end of each day, was his cup of tea. Now he was home, of course, he could get some decent grub. Mind you, he told me, the corned beef sandwiches could taste really good after a day mucking about in the desert . . .

15

Listening to the radio one evening, Cass learned that in the USA, two hundred thousand people had gathered in cities like New York and San Francisco to protest against the American involvement in the Vietnam War. The violence in Aden was a little scrap, a skirmish, when compared with Vietnam. Servicemen were being shot in Aden, but in acceptable numbers.

The information Cass and his colleagues received regarding terrorist attacks in Aden was scant. The BBC World Service gave out more than the local radio. British troops in Aden had no Joan Baez or Bob Dylan to sing protest songs on their behalf. People back home were not calling for their return. The scale of the activities in Aden was not sufficient to arouse the anger of the masses. So the soldiers, airmen and sailors had to play out the scenario set for them by politicians and generals. Young men from counties in England, Scotland, Wales and Ireland were being attacked from behind by terrorists, and from the front by their own media. They were both victims and aggressors, and yet they were neither. They were simply confused boys wondering why they had ever walked into a recruiting office in Sheffield, or Glasgow, or Cardiff, or Belfast, when they could have been at home, sitting in a pub and reading about what they were doing now and shrugging along with the rest of the drinkers.

When Cass was not working gathering radio intelligence, or on sentry duty in the watchtower, he spent most of his time swimming at the Mermaid Club. It had changed very little since he was last there as a boy of fourteen, when it had been called the Lido. The net to keep out the sharks and other dangerous fish, which extended in an open square out into the sea, was still the same shape and size that he remembered it. The swimming pool looked the same and he recognized one or two of the drinks waiters. In fact Susanne had been impressed when Tarik, a waiter who had once gently rebuked Cass's mother for not making Cass wear a shirt, brought a bottle of suntan lotion "free of charge" to her as she lay on the beach.

"What's this for?" she asked, looking up from a supine position.

"For rubbing on tummy," said Tarik, pointing to the white space between her bikini top and bottom. "You will burn otherwise, like this one, when he was a boy so high," he flattened a hand about four feet from the ground, "and the terror of all the waiters here."

Then Tarik walked back to the clubhouse.

"What *was* all that about?" she asked Cass, who was lying next to her, a grin on his face.

"Oh, when my mother brought me here as a boy, the first day we arrived in Aden, I burned rather badly. Got huge blisters over my back. Still have the scars." He showed her. "Tarik kept an eye on me after that and if he saw me going pink he'd tell my mother to put a shirt on me. She was incensed the first time, and told him to mind his own business, but it didn't put him off and gradually she did as she was told. Some of these people are like that. They wear down your resistance like rain will wear away a soft rock."

"They *erode* you, you mean?"

Cass used some of the lotion on himself and some on Susanne, then left the bottle sticking up in the sand, by the razor-shells they had collected. She had already remarked on his fascination with beachcombing. He told her it had been with him since he was a boy. Cass liked to get up around dawn on days when he wasn't working and walk along the safe beaches, his head down and eyes fixed on the tidemarks, looking for the ocean's bounty. Especially after a storm, which threw more than usual up on to the sands. To find a rarish one, like the blue Jester cowrie he had found tucked in some weed the other day, helped to lift the spirits.

"It's like looking for treasure," he explained. "I like to walk, but I have to do something else, while I'm walking. When I'm on the beach, I look for shells. Gastropods or bivalves, it's all the same to me. Turbans, murexes, slippers, cones, conches, cowries, you name it, I've collected it. I've got over three hundred different types at home."

"Really?" She gave an extravagant yawn.

He laughed. "That's the difference between us," he said. "I find this sort of thing tremendously exciting and you find it boring."

"Because you're a man and I'm a . . . "

"Nothing to do with gender," he said, firmly. "It's to do with whether you were a third-culture child or not."

Susanne rolled over on to her back to listen, as Cass tried to explain what he meant, at the same time studying her form.

She had a small athletic body: trim and compact. She looked vulnerable sometimes, making him feel protective, but was actually quite tough underneath. Her outlook was normally practical, though sometimes emotion could take precedence. She was fiercely loyal and, once loved, would love back with intensity. She was intelligent, though not an intellectual. She had a spirit that, were it visible, was like a lantern whose rays reached far beyond her own self and helped light the souls of others.

This was the kind of woman Cass had always wanted, though his head was stuffed with the nonsense of masculine mythology, and could have got in the way of his heart. It was lucky for him that he considered neither head nor heart, but followed his instincts. His instinct was to fall gradually in love with the woman by his side.

Susanne Williams was the descendant of Welsh ancestors who had moved from Wales in the middle of the nineteenth century to put their mining skills to work in the lead mines of Swaledale, in Yorkshire. By the time the galena had run out they had turned one or two bright members of the family into veterinary surgeons. One of these was Susanne's father, Lawrence Williams, who had married the daughter of a Catholic Yorkshire businessman, Mary Stokeley. Mary had inherited her father's head for business, which she could apply to the profession of veterinarian, as well as to merchandising. Discovering that there was a glut of vets in Yorkshire at the time, Mary persuaded Lawrence, who despite his ancestors was as Yorkshire as the River Swale itself, to move down to Wales where there were fewer members of his profession. Mary argued that the rugged scenery of the Welsh valleys was much the same as that of the Yorkshire dales. Turfed hills and dry-stone walls were the same anywhere, she said.

So Mary and Lawrence moved to Wales, where they had three children, the eldest of which was Susanne. Lawrence never converted to Catholicism, he was not even sold on the Methodism practised by his forebears. Any religion which did not take into consideration the possibility that *all* animals had souls, was not worth the time of day so far as he was concerned. Lawrence had tended animals and birds since he was twelve and was convinced that creatures both wild and domestic were possessed of a spirit. He left the education of their children to his wife and though he would have nothing to do with Christianity himself, he placed no obstacles in the way of his children. They could make up their own minds later in life. Lawrence was not an atheist, nor even an agnostic, he was a believer without an established religion.

The two boys went to local schools, but Susanne was sent to a convent where she was taught fear and love, in that order. When she left school her mother intended her to be a doctor, but Susanne was not an academic. She herself actually wanted to work in publishing, but compromised with her mother's plans, and went into nursing instead. After a year in a general hospital she applied and was accepted for Queen Alexandra's Nursing Corps, and was subsequently sent to Aden. She now felt she was out of the influence and beyond the range of her parents' domineering ways. In this she was utterly mistaken. They would always, even beyond their deaths, exert indirect control over her life. She would forever be trying to impress them, gain their approval, and would never ever be able to even dent the helmet of criticism such parents find it impossible to doff.

Susanne had the kind of parents to whom praise did not come easily. She and her brothers had never been able to do anything quite well enough to elicit a favourable response from their mother and father. A school report with straight A's, except perhaps for one slot – say geography, which earned a C – would be scrutinized and then, instead of, "Well done, look at all those A's!" would come, "We'll have to do something about geography, won't we? Surely you can do better than a C?" Susanne's youngest brother had rebelled right from the start and refused to spend his life desperately seeking favour where none was to be had. He was now, at seventeen, working in a London restaurant as a waiter. The second eldest had failed to get into Cambridge, but had entered King's College, London, and was on his way to being a lawyer. Susanne, and everyone else, knew that he would make it, but Mary and Lawrence Williams had not expressed one word of praise. They still wondered, usually out loud, why he had failed to impress the Cambridge Board.

When she had told Cass of the trials she had with her parents, Cass showed surprise. He had never actually thought about his relationship with his mother and father. It was there, it existed, but it was not something to ponder over, certainly not something to get anxious about. He was like some political ingénu who has just been lectured by a fervent idealist and feels that until now he has not taken the world seriously enough.

"My parents praised *everything* I did," he explained to Susanne. "I took it for granted. I mean, right from the moment I used my potty for the first time, they've done nothing but tell me how clever I am. I suppose their expectations are so low, being from farmer-fisher folk, that all I had to do was learn to read and write. You see, my dad got away from the land and the sea, and though he was only a sergeant in the RAF that made him the big success story of the family. All I have to do is surpass that . . . "

When they were ready to go home, they gathered up their beach mats and left the beach for the pavilion. Just as they were climbing the steps there was a mortar attack on the Mermaid Club.

After the first explosion, some hundred yards offshore, Cass and Susanne huddled behind a pillar, Cass peering round the stonework to watch the bombs zigzag towards the beach. Mesmerized by the great fountains of spray, it was only at the last minute that the adrenaline did its job and had him whipping his head out of danger. On the beach a young man had not been quick enough and caught a line of shrapnel around his belly when the mortars reached the shore. Cass watched as the boy writhed in the sand, unwittingly boring himself the hole that might have saved him a few moments earlier.

Susanne went to help the young man, but an ambulance was on the spot within a few minutes. She returned to Cass's side and, shaken, they made their way back to their quarters. Then he left her and climbed the hill to his own billets, full of the news, only to find Blue 16 weeping.

"What's up, Blue?" he asked, sitting on the edge of the older man's bed. Luckily there was no one at their end of the balcony at the time, or Blue 16 would have suffered taunts.

The little chubby man was sitting cross-legged on his bed, the flesh on his belly creased like a Buddha's. He lifted his tear-stained face and said, "I wanna go home, Cass. I wanna see my kids. I want my wife . . . "

Cass was embarrassed. He found counselling difficult.

"It's okay, mate, you'll be on your way soon. Look at your chuff chart. There's more days gone than to do."

"But each day gets longer, harder. In the beginning days were just days, now they're bloody *weeks*, and the weeks are like, I dunno, like bloody forevers. This ain't right, Cass. This is no way to live, without your family, not seeing your kids grow up.

166

And what about my missus? Trying to raise two tots on her own, stuck out at that transit camp? It's all right for them who have parents or in-laws to live with, but we don't get on with ours. She's on her own, stuck out in the middle of Norfolk on an old disused airbase. Sure, there's other wives there, but still it's not right, is it?"

Cass agreed it was not right and at least Blue 16 had stopped crying. Cass suggested they go out and have a beer, and reluctantly, because he was in some perverse way enjoying his depression, Blue 16 agreed.

"Did you hear about the Stones?" he said to Cass, as they made their way down the hill. "They're up on drugs charges, back in the UK. Been taken to court."

"S'probably some publicity stunt," said Cass.

"Maybe. Still, they're bad boys all right, ain't they?"

"Not as bad as the boys we have to deal with."

Cass was talking of the NLF and FLOSY terrorists, who had stepped up their campaigns, both against each other and against the British. That weekend there had been forty-seven grenade attacks, seventeen shootings, two mortar attacks, with nine local nationals killed, one serviceman killed, several wounded on all sides, and seventy locals put in detention. Saladin armoured cars were evident as peacekeepers, but orders did not permit the use of their weapons. Only small-arms fire could be used in retaliation by the security forces. The British forces were now ferrying wives and families back to the UK, relieving some of the security forces of the duties of protecting them. Blue 16 was particularly aggrieved that he had had to risk his life guarding the wives of other men, while his own had not been allowed to join him.

"After we've had a few beers," said Cass, entering the Naafi bar, "we'll go and find Jasmine's and lose our virginity."

"More likely to lose our bollocks," said Blue 16, gloomily. "Or our heads."

"Well, the anticipation will be worth it."

They played this game every time they went into the seedy-looking bar, as if they were going on to some place afterwards, where they could lose themselves in an orgy of sex and drugs and rock-'n'-roll. What they really had in store was a long drunken walk back up the hill to a sterile balcony where they would roll a couple of cigarettes made of pure Dunhill, and then flop off to sleep, knowing that the next day would be full of dust and heat, and boredom.

16

The minutes hand was tickling midnight. I had just finished
reading a Classics Comic called *The Masque of the Red Death* by
Edgar Allan Poe, and was preparing to settle down comfortably
to a nightmare, when I suddenly decided I needed to go to the
toilet. I lay there under the single white sheet for another half an
hour, getting my courage into some sort of order, then finally
made my way along the stone landing. Everything was whitewashed plaster-over-concrete in Aden houses, the floors were
tiled and even the bannisters were brick under the plaster. Those
solid villas, with their arched doorways and lattice brickwork on
the desert side to encourage throughflow of breezes, were made
the way I imagined a Mexican hacienda is built, of cool stone
with high ceilings and lots of white space. There was no wood to
be had in this corner of Arabia, but there was plenty of sand and
sufficient water. All that needed to be imported was the cement.
Consequently there was no flexibility in the buildings. Nothing
moved, nothing creaked in the house, everywhere was utterly
silent, save for the clicking of beetles or chitchat lizards. Incon-
gruously, this made me feel more insecure, as if I was in some
dead place, a tomb, where the floor might open up at any moment
to swallow me whole.

My feet slip-slapped on the tiled floor as I made as much
noise as I could. Mum called out sleepily, "Who's that?" and her
voice sent a ripple of relief through me.

"Only Cass," I whispered. "Going to the toilet."

She grunted and presumably fell off to sleep again. My middle brother Richie walked in his sleep, so she always woke up and asked who it was. When we first moved to the house, on the second or third night, Richie had got up, stumbled into my parents' bedroom, and piddled over the bedside table before Mum could lead him to the right place. Richie worked out later, with the aid of a floor plan, that Mum's bedside table (in the new house) was where the toilet used to be (in the old house) if you reversed everything exactly.

"Which makes sense, don't it, Mum," he had said, " 'cause we're in the southern hemisphere here. It's like a mirror image, isn't it?"

Mum said, yes, that must be it. She was proud of him for working that out. I hadn't the heart to tell either of them we were still in the northern hemisphere, even though we had come a long way south. Why spoil their fun? Mum probably knew anyway.

On my way back to bed I noticed that the red ants had killed a cockroach close to the border and were carrying it with great display before the very noses of their enemies. I stood and watched for a few minutes, thinking this was pretty foolish of the reds, unless they wanted to provoke an incident. Sure enough, as they were bearing their prize triumphantly onward, towards a crack in the concrete stairs, an incensed army of black ants surged forward. I couldn't hear the battle cries of course, but I could sense the righteous fury of the attackers. When they drew nearer to the waiting reds, the blacks seemed to separate into clans, as the main mass broke into little bunches. Then out of the fissures poured further reds, as if they had been waiting for this moment. It was definitely an ambush. The blacks had been set up for this and since they had to negotiate a high cliff in the form of a stair rise, the reds had the advantage. They began to slaughter the blacks with mechanical efficiency as the latter fell amongst them, not bothering to enter black territory, but just waiting for the clans to cross the border.

I was appalled at this massacre, though I had long since made

170

a vow never to interfere in the policies of either the reds or the blacks. I felt they had to work out their own destinies, without any interference from gi-ants. In any case, a few weeks previously I had seen the film *Them!*, where an atomic explosion causes ants to grow to twelve feet in height. They start attacking humans and biting off their heads. I intended to play it safe, so that if this fiction ever became fact I could yell at them, "I never touched you, when I was big . . . !"

The next morning I woke with my head still on. There was a two-inch camel spider on the windowsill, sunning itself, and I said, "You won't last long, mate, once the ants know you're here." I thought it looked at me with contempt.

I went along the landing to the bathroom. The ants were milling around in the corners, eating the white powder Mum used to put down to kill them. They seemed to thrive on it. She had once tried boiling water from a kettle, but the idea of writhing bodies had revolted all of us, so she never did it again.

"Camel spider, in the bedroom," I said to the ants, crooking a thumb in the direction behind me. I felt no loyalty towards arachnids.

After I had washed and dressed I met Dix and we walked in the heat and dust to Heather's house, where her father had promised us a treat. He was a meteorological officer and had once been part of an Arctic Survey team. He was waiting for us on their balcony, standing awkwardly because of his bad back, looking like someone who has been broken in two and put back together just slightly off-true. He was a powerful-looking man though, and I would have hated to cross him in any way. Despite his back I was sure he could break a bull in two over his thick knees.

Heather was there.

"Hello boys," she said, brightly.

"Hello Heather," we mumbled back, always shy with her when either of her parents was around. She was wearing a pretty flowered dress, her plaits hanging down the front, past the square neckline, over her small bust. She was trim and neat, as usual. Brian was somewhere out the back. We could hear his air rifle popping away. He had no doubt told his father he was shooting at paper targets, but we knew he fired at kite hawks that descended to root around dustbins with the pi-dogs. He would have shot at pi-dogs too, except that once upon a time, in the days when he did, one of them didn't run away, but turned on him. We went round to say hello and found him lying prone on the ground aiming at a breakfast cereal carton.

"Hi Brian," I said.

"Hi yerself," he said, and swung the rifle in the direction of a ragged brown kite hawk at the last moment. "And no, you can't have a shot. It's my gun. Go and play with my sister." The gun popped and a little spray of sand went up near the kite hawk, which hopped away sideways on one leg in an alarmed manner.

This little creep would have been hammered into the ground by either Dix or myself a long time ago, if he were not the brother of our beloved Heather. My fingers itched to grab him by the collar and drag him somewhere where I could pummel his fat little face.

"No need to be like that, Brian," said Dix, the edge of his voice sharp enough to cut through leather. As we walked away, Dix, either accidentally or on purpose, trod on the fleshy part of Brian's leg.

"Ow!" yelled the victim, then with his face contorted, he twisted round in the sand and pointed the gun at us. My stomach turned over. Air-rifle slugs bloody well hurt.

Dix's voice was full of menace.

"Pull the trigger, Brian. Go on. Pull the trigger! I'll ram the gun down your throat."

This was not likely to frighten Brian.

"If you do," I said, "I'll put a whipsnake in your bed. You know I'll do *that*!"

Gradually the rifle was lowered. We left him there, glowering at us. Dix said, "What happens if you dangle a Brian by its tail?" and I dutifully replied, "Its piggy little eyes drop out."

We walked away and round to the front of the house.

"Ready boys?" said Mr McNiece. "Said hello to Brian?"

"We've said hello," replied Dix in a deadpan voice.

"Good. Let's be off then."

Mr McNiece had a bullnose Morris and we were to be given a ride to the Met. Office in this shiny vehicle. Heather waved goodbye and went indoors, as we pulled out on to the empty sandstrewn roads which led to Steamer Point.

Mr McNiece was taking us to his office, to show us all the instruments and weather charts he worked with. This treat was to make up for the fact that we had been thrown out of the officers' swimming pool because we were rankers' kids, even though Mr and Mrs McNiece had taken us with them. Mr McNiece, I suppose being a civilian of officer status, was incensed by this class prejudice. He argued with the club steward, but failed to make any impression.

We were taken to the weather station where we met Mr Patterson, a small white-haired man with a nervous smile.

"Hello, boys," he said cheerily. "Come to see where the weather's made, eh?"

We laughed at that.

The ceiling fans were going full blast, blowing up the corners of papers. I was amazed at the number of charts scattered around the room on high tables. Men in shorts and rolled-up shirtsleeves sat on high stools and dipped pens into inks of many colours. Then they scratched away at the charts, writing tiny figures all over them. A dozen Bob Cratchits who had no need for coal, sweated away as if they were doing some violent physical exercise.

We were shown the charts, with their red, black, blue and green figures, which we were told were isobars and isotherms. Masses and masses of figures. My mum always said why bother having met. men in Aden when you knew every day was going to be hot and humid? Here was the answer. The weather was not

173

just a matter of sunshine or rain, but of complex wind patterns, atmospheric pressures, cloud bases, and all that kind of thing. Ships needed to know whether a storm was imminent. Aircraft needed to know about clouds.

I found the charts magical. They were like ever-changing maps of some kingdom in the sky. I felt that if I could crack the codes, they would lead me to some place of great treasure, or to a land peopled by fabulous beasts, like giants.

We were shown the equipment too, which was just as fascinating. Wind-speed recorders, barometers, chronometers, lovely tactile objects made of brass and glass, with finely-tuned mechanisms, springs, ratchets, wheels. What made them so precious was the fact that they were fashioned oh-so precisely. They were solid objects that shone in the sunlight like precious metal, yet their scales were made to measure the finest of marks. When you touched one, you knew you were handling an instrument that was handcrafted by an artistic scientist, probably with great pride and love. I derived the same feeling from the meteorological instruments that I do from antique clocks.

We were told many magic words, such as troposphere, mesosphere, exosphere, Kennelly-Heaviside layer, Appleton layer, Van Allen belt. There were cyclones, depressions and anticyclones, and rain was called by its witch-given names, like *precipitation*.

The men in this room were the weather prophets and at that moment both Dix and I wanted to be nothing else but one of these great wizards who interpreted the voice of the wind, who could translate airstreams into patterns on charts, who could paraphrase the clouds. On their wonderful charts they caged the waves, they captured the storms, they imprisoned the mighty forces of the earth and sea.

"That was *really* good," said Dix fervently, to Mr McNiece, as we left the building.

"*Really* good," I echoed.

Mr McNiece smiled at our obvious awe.

"I know, I felt the same way when I was first taken into a met.

174

room. I suppose that's why I'm a met. man now. Shouldn't be surprised if you two go the same way."

We both said we intended to.

That afternoon we went to the Lido, just Dix and I, to practise in the pool for the school sports. I had also entered for the hundred yards running race, but Dix had declined to put himself in that event. I think he knew I would beat him. Abdulla had been helping me train, running along Khormaksar beach. He was a good trainer, firm but helpful. Dix had watched one or two training sessions and had quietly backed out of the race, which I took as a good sign. My most dangerous rival was Mick Gophner, who had skinny legs but a big stride. On the other hand I knew I could not win against Dix at swimming, but I still wanted to try.

The pool at the Lido was raised high above the beach and situated alongside the clubhouse. We began warm-ups by just cruising up and down for about eight lengths. Then we practised sprints, using the Australian crawl. Dix then went on to do butterfly stroke, which I could never get the hang of, while I practised breaststroke. Dix thought breaststroke was a drippy thing to do, and he hardly ever used it, though he was good at it. Finally, when we were exhausted, we did some diving from the springboard and from the high board. When I used the high board the water hurt my head. I've never been able to do a high dive without coming away with a splitting headache. Dix said it never bothered him.

We were both standing on the high-board platform, lazily chatting in the hot sun. Down below us was the stretch of beach immediately in front of the Lido clubhouse. There were figures sunning themselves on the sand, calling for drinks, yelling at young children. The beach extended beyond the Lido, on either side, into military administration areas. Others were also using these strips of sand, probably to get away from the crowds within the Lido. There was a lot of squealing going on, amongst the kids and even among the young women, whose boyfriends

175

threatened to throw them in the water every so often. If you closed your eyes, you would swear you were in a livestock market sometimes, which is probably why we didn't hear any screams.

I saw a flurry in the water, I remember that. Though the day was a little windy and there were some white horses on the ocean, flicking up spume in odd places. One flurry of surf is much like another. So I probably didn't take a great deal of notice of it, being more intent on watching someone snorkelling in my favourite spot, out by the rocks, wondering if he was getting any good shells.

Then we heard a commotion down on the beach, outside the shark net. I could see something floating in the water. On the beach itself a little boy was crying. Then a passing native canoe swung its bows near the flotsam. The fisherman in the dugout leapt into the froth and began beating the surface of the sea, using his paddle like a club. It was almost as if he were trying to create some sort of bubbling wash. The depth of the water only reached just above his knees, which, once we knew what had happened, seemed incredibly shallow. I think that was the most frightening aspect of it: how little water it took.

We observed this strange behaviour in silence, realizing something very peculiar was going on, but not comprehending its meaning.

Men came running from Nissen huts close to the shore, and others went round the corner of the shark net, to get to the open beach. Three of them went into the water, and you could see they were scared of something, because they moved like automatons. The fisherman waded to shore, while the three men grabbed the floating object and pulled on it. None of them seemed to want to carry it bodily, because they each kept one of their arms away from the thing, sort of dangling by their side, while the other gripped the item. As they pulled the object through the water, still very jerkily, we could see the smoky trail of red it left behind.

Inside the Lido fence, though the tanning, beach games and

176

swimming were still in progress, people started to drift towards the end where the three marionettes were jerking their way to the strand. I don't think anyone called out "Hey, look at this!" or drew attention to that side of the beach. When a tragedy occurs there seems to be some kind of instinct which primes people's curiosity. It's the ripple that goes through the herd of deer sensing danger. It's the one-in-a-thousand sound which has the sleeping cat instantly alert. Soon a whole crowd of people was poised over the spot where the puppetmen would leave the water.

A hand was waved, as if at flies, by one of the three. They hauled, rather than lifted, their cargo up on to a blanket that was spread like a picnic cloth on the sand. The crowd leaned forward, then the front lines lurched backwards, causing a roll like a wave to go through the spectators. I could see what was on the blanket then: a woman – or more accurately – half a woman. The left leg, arm and some of her left flank were gone. The wound was wide and raw: a mixture of grey, red and white.

I felt dizzy and clutched the rail to stop myself from falling to the ground. Dix's eyes were squinting, and I remembered he couldn't see well without his glasses. He leaned right forward, as if pressing one eye to a keyhole.

"What is it?" he asked. "A fish?"

I gagged, saying, "A woman."

"No, it's not a woman," he said in a definite tone, as if I had asked a question instead of making a statement.

"It's a woman, Dix. I – I think a shark's got her."

People were pointing out to sea now, as if at some dorsal fin cutting through the water, but I could see nothing out there. The white horses had increased in number, but there was no great fish heading out to sea, nor cruising in the shallows. From where we were I could actually see the sandy bottom of the bay at the place where she had been attacked.

Someone had his hand resting on the Arab fisherman's shoulder. The thin brown figure, bare but for a loincloth, still had his paddle in his hand and he was looking down on the woman as if he couldn't believe she was dead. I suppose he jumped into the water purely as a reaction to someone needing help. An unconscious impulse, of the kind that made Lord Jim into a coward first and a hero later. Such motivation did not diminish the fisherman's courage, for there are few such actions which are not prompted from behind the brain, rather than from within it. The fact was, he had risked his life to drive off the shark, beating it with his small paddle. Perhaps he also saw himself lying there, soaking the blanket in useless blood, and was horrified at his own heroism.

Dix said, "I'm gonna get my glasses," in a highly excited tone. He scrambled down the steps and ran to the dressing rooms. I followed on, very slowly, my legs trembling so much I almost fell a couple of times. I knew Dix would want to go and inspect the remains of the corpse. All I wanted to do was get as far away from it as possible.

While I was dressing he returned from his visit to the site of the body and sat down hard on the bench. He seemed angry.

"Took her away," he said, "before I got there. Just saw the stretcher being shoved in the ambulance."

"Think yourself lucky," I snapped, which made him look at me in surprise.

"It was a shark," he said, looking into my face, all his anger gone. "I've never seen someone ate by a shark."

"Well you have now."

"Not really. You saw it, I didn't."

"Think yourself lucky," I repeated, inanely, but he believed there was some sort of warped pride behind my words, as if I were using them to dramatize the incident.

"Yeah," he said, nodding, "I know what you mean. Nex' time I'm gonna keep my glasses nearby, then I won't miss it."

17

Mum came home that evening and said her boss had received a telephone call and had gone terribly pale, dropped the phone, and had staggered out of the office. By the time work was over for the day, he still had not returned.

"I don't know what it's all about," she said, dishing out the greens which had been cooked to a single sodden lump by Said, who was off us at the moment – something to do with his holiday, I don't know what – and getting at us in subtle ways. "He looked like a ghost. All I heard him say was 'My wife' or something like that. Do you think she's been, you know –" Mum stopped abruptly and indicated us boys with her eyes to show Dad she couldn't finish the question but any adult half attending would have known what the missing words were. Actually all of us kids did too, even Duggy, but of course we never let on.

Innuendo, however, wouldn't have hit Dad if he'd been as big as a barn. He ignored Mum's question, but at the same time answered it by getting his own news in.

He said, "I heard someone was attacked by a shark in the Lido. It got through the netting somehow."

Mum glared at him, then a thought struck her.

"Do you think that's his wife, my boss's wife?"

"It didn't get through the netting," I said. "It was outside. I saw it."

In a practised move, Mum suddenly picked up the springy breadknife, flipped it round so she was holding it by the end of the blade, and rapped Richie's fingers with the handle. He had

179

been reaching for his pudding before the rest of us had finished the first course. Mum was very impressive when it came to discipline. She knew the value of showmanship.

"Ouch!" cried Richie, whipping both hands into his lap.

"Manners, young man," she said, then turned to me. "You *saw* it? What did you see?"

"I saw the woman brought out of the sea. There was only half of her. Shark got the rest."

Mum went pale, looked at Dad, and then said, "You boys are *never* to go down that Lido again!"

"Aw, Mum," I protested. "She was outside the shark net. We never swim outside the shark net."

"I heard she was only in shallow water, up to her knees," said Dad. This of course did not help my cause at all. Dad was good at remaining in some other, distant world but managing to get across a destructive message every so often, which ensured that turmoil always reigned in this one. I looked daggers at him but he had gone back to eating his dinner.

Mum was adamant: we were never to go to the Lido again, ever. I resigned myself to at least a week of being forbidden to go into the sea, until she had talked with other people about the incident, and had calmed down a little. *Never* and *ever* had short lives in our family.

After dinner we had a quiz game, which ended in uproar because Dad, who was not paying attention as usual, had asked Richie, "Who is buried in the tomb of the Unknown Soldier?"

"The Unknown Soldier of course," crowed Richie, realizing Dad had muddled question and answer together.

"Yes, but which one?" asked Dad, trying to save himself, and we all collapsed in laughter.

Just before I was due to go to bed, Mum gave me a note for Mrs McNiece: something about the Women's Guild.

"Trot that round, will you, dear?" she said. "It'll be good practice for Sports Day."

I dutifully took the message and set out for the McNiece

household, thinking I would have a legitimate reason to see Heather without my sidekick sharing half the conversation and attention. However, as I drew nearer to the house, my heart began to pound. I was working myself up into a state where I knew I would not be able to say a thing.

There was no one on the veranda, but I could see the living-room light on and climbed the steps. The French windows were open and I could sense someone to the left of them, just out of my sight. My heart was still running around in my chest like a rabbit, so I waited for a few seconds in order to calm down. Then I rapped on the glass of the French windows. Mrs McNiece appeared immediately, a hairbrush in her right hand.

"Oh, it's Cass," she said, frowning a little. "What are you doing here at this hour, Cass?"

She knew it was not my night for visiting Heather.

"My mother sent me with a message. I've to give this to you and go straight back home," I said, handing over the note.

She took it and moved back. "Come inside for a moment, Cass," she said, reading it, "I might need to reply."

I stepped over the threshold and glanced left. Heather was sitting in a wooden straight-backed chair wearing her nightdress. It was a long shift which covered her more than any frock I had seen her wear, but still I was intensely embarrassed. What astounded me though, was her hair. Her mother had unravelled the plaits I was used to seeing, and now her light brown hair hung loose, down to her waist. She looked breathtakingly pretty, and the sight of this amazing princess made me feel light-headed. I felt giddy. I was in Rapunzel's bower, blinding beauty before me, and nothing behind but a long drop.

"Hello, Cass," she said, brightly. "How are you?"

"Fine," I gulped. "You, er, you've got really long hair haven't you?"

She fingered the strands, crinkled where they had been in plaits, self-consciously.

"It's a nuisance," she said. "Mother has to brush it out every night."

"It's nice," I defended the hair to its owner.

I would have defended that hair against a thousand giants. At that moment, Heather was not the Heather I knew, but an unapproachable young Scottish beauty, a lass of the glens. I looked into those Gaelic eyes and I saw the woman that Robert Burns had been writing about in every one of his love poems, whether she was called Jean or Mary, or whatever. My heart sank too, for I believed that I could never hope to keep such a woman, when she was fully grown. Heather would marry a prince, not a pauper. I had to make the most of our time together as childhood sweethearts, sharing her with my best friend at the same time.

"It looks as bonnie as a braw simmer's day, so dinna fash yersel'," I said, escaping into my well-practised "Burns" accent.

Mrs McNiece glanced up from the note.

"That's very gude, Cass," she said, getting a little broader herself. "You sound more Scottish than me."

"You should hear him recite 'Scots W'hae!'," said Heather, proudly.

I returned home with the reply in something of a daze. Until now Heather had just been a very good friend, one I liked enormously well, but from that moment on I was deeply in love with her. It made life difficult, because when I mentioned it shyly to my mum, she told me in a kindly way not to be so silly.

"You can't fall in love at your age," she said.

Lord what liars these adults be!

They tell the young that *real* love is something felt only by adults.

What utter lies, what perfidy, what *treachery*.

Because those private feelings we had for each other were so wonderful and powerful, we were afraid of them. We believed the adults and thought ourselves to be freaks of nature for having such strange emotions. It forced us to remain silent, to treat our affections as a joke. We did not wish to be mocked as sentimental. We looked upon love as a passing childhood illness that would leave no scars.

What a terrible waste. They *should* have told us we would never again have the same capacity to love. They should have told us that when we were grown we would be too fearful to open ourselves completely, too selfish to give without receiving. They should have told us that the purity of pubescent love would soon enough be corroded.

They should have told *me* that when the vagaries of military life scattered our families over the globe, I would never see Heather again, and that I would look for her, or merely signs of her, in all other women for the rest of my life. That the feelings I had for her were as real as they were strong.

What shocking waste is caused by adults' lies.

On the day of the school sports a piper was playing as the spectators gathered on the hard-baked earth maidan between the school house and the officers' married quarters. One of the tunes he played was "The Kilworth Hills", and he followed this with "The Barren Rocks of Aden". It was like most bagpipe music, immensely stirring. Whenever I heard the pipes, I was so uplifted by their martial air that I would have marched and died for Scotland, and I wasn't even Scottish.

Abdulla was saying to me, "Now remember, you run and run, and not look back. Like we did on the beach. Keep up your head. Keep it up high. If you look back, you waste time, and someone behind thinks you are worried, yes?"

"Okay, okay." I was getting nervous and he must have sensed it for he grinned. "You will win, my friend. I know this. You have not to worry."

I smiled at him. "Thanks, Abdulla, you're a brick."

"You are my very good friend," he said, seriously.

183

"I know."

We had a lot of waiting around to do, of course. I had entered for the hundred yards, the javelin and the long jump. Dix was in the javelin too, which was my first event. My parents weren't allowed inside the arena, but I could see them sitting in chairs by the marquee. Mum was in a white shirtwaister with a pretty white hat. Dad was in uniform: khaki short-sleeved shirt and long khaki shorts. In those days the stocking tops almost met the hem of the shorts. His uniforms were always starched to a brittle texture and his collar left raw marks where it had cut into his neck. He didn't seem to mind the discomfort and evinced surprise when the wounds were pointed out to him by Mum.

Heather was doing the high jump, but I didn't watch her from the edge of the sandpit because she said it would make her nervous if we did. So I kept account of her from afar. I don't think she did very well, but she didn't disgrace herself. She had these strong-looking thighs, but was no antelope.

Surprisingly, Bags Williams won the javelin, with Dix coming second. I came fourth, behind someone else. I was hopeless in the long jump and got knocked out very early. By the time my race came round, I was feeling despondent. Abdulla came across to me, but was shooed away by one of the schoolteachers, who said Arab boys were really not supposed to be there. I could have killed her.

"How are you feeling, son?" said Dad, when I went across to them to get my best white plimsolls, for the race. Mum had bought them for me last Christmas, but I only used them for running in. The rest of the time I wore the old black ones, with holes in them.

"Fine," I mumbled.

Mum said, "Richie won throwing the cricket ball for his age-group."

"Did he?" I was surprised. I never thought Richie was good at anything in those days.

"Won it by a mile," said Dad.

184

I tied the laces of my pumps slowly, looking for Heather. Although she hadn't wanted us to watch her, I wanted her to see me in my race. I had plenty of style and even if I lost (please God no) I would look good doing it. I thought.

I heard the call over the tannoy for us to line up at the start. I crossed the maidan to the track, which was a piece of ground marked out alongside the football field. Mick Gophner was already there, doing limbering-up exercises.

"You ready to get dust up your snout?" he asked. "Look at this . . . " he held up his foot so that I could see the sole " . . . that's what you'll be starin' at when I cross the line."

My heart sank. He was wearing the latest in running shoes, with spikes and all. He was probably a lot better than I had previously given him credit for, because no parent will spend the kind of money those shoes cost unless their son is a serious athlete. I felt self-conscious in my white pumps, thinking now how inadequate they were. I began to pray that Heather would not be watching as I was humbled before a crowd of hundreds.

"I think I'm good enough to beat you," I said.

He laughed. "No chance, sunshine. I've been out every night for the last six months, trainin', haven't I Mac?"

"Every night for the last six months," repeated Mac.

"And how have I done?" said Mick.

"Brilliant," said Mac.

"See what I mean?" he said to me. "No chance. Come back tomorrow when nobody's here. You'll be a winner then, my son. This afternoon belongs to the Gophners."

"On your marks!" called the starter.

I shuffled up to the line, a white powdermark, and bent my knees slightly. My hands were bunched, my arms in a boxer's pose, as I prepared to fling myself forward.

"Get set!"

Mick Gophner elbowed me slightly, grinning when I looked up.

"GO!"

185

I shot forward, all thoughts of the twins gone. I could feel my legs going and I knew even before I had gone ten yards that the race was won. I was out in front and no one, wearing running shoes or not, was going to pass *me*.

Fifty yards down the track I stumbled a little, but kept my feet, the momentum carrying me forward. I was aware of a figure on either side of me. One of them had to be Mick, but I was damned if I was going to look. Abdulla had said "keep your eyes on the tape" and that's exactly what I intended to do.

Five yards before the tape I knew that Gophner was getting ready to pass me and I put on an extra little burst of speed. I heard him gasp, then he was gone, and I was through the finish line. People were patting me on the back. One of them was Mr McNiece, who said, "Well run, Cass." My dad was there too, his eyes shining. The only time I had seen his face so radiant was when my uncle had won the competition for the straightest furrow at the Young Farmers' Agricultural Fair. I had my hands on my knees, gasping for breath, looking up. I wanted to see Heather. Then I found her, standing shyly by her mother. She smiled at me: the kind of smile men will climb Everest to win. I was happy. I trotted away to do my warm-downs, waving to Abdulla, who was now on the other side of the fence jumping up and down, his teeth flashing. I ran over to him.

"How was that?"

"Very good, my friend. Very, very good."

"You did it for me," I said, in a rare burst of honesty. "I wouldn't have done it otherwise."

He laughed. "We did it together. I go tell my father, we won the hundred yards. Goodbye, Cass. See you later."

" 'Bye Abdulla. And thanks, mate."

He ran off, his thin legs pumping hard. He was faster than me. I could see that at a glance. He was faster than me, I think, but he was an Arab. I thought about asking Skip if we could have a scouts' Sports Day, so the Arabs and Indians could compete too. There were only white kids at our school.

Then something thumped me hard in the back and pain went shooting up my spine. I yelled and spun round, to find Mick Gophner behind me, foaming at the mouth.

"You bloody tripped me!" he accused.

I didn't answer, but the pain from his punch drew a swift reaction from me, and I hit him in the face. He shook it off and came wading in with hooked arms. I felt blows to the chest and neck, before I lashed out again, connecting with his hard bony head. Then someone attacked me from the side: his twin brother Mac. Before I could reply to this, I was aware of Dix beside me, lashing out at Mac. The four of us windmilled, fell in the dust together, struggling like a collapsed rugby pack.

Then strong hands wrenched us apart. Adults were saying things like, "Disgraceful, ought to be ashamed of yourselves," and the Gophner twins were dragged one way, Dix and I the other. Skip was there, stern and unyielding. He let us cool off, about ten yards apart, then brought us all together.

"Shake hands," he said, "so they can all see you."

"Like hell," snarled Mick Gophner.

"Shake hands or you're out of the scout group," said Skip.

"He tripped me in the race."

Dix said, "You tripped yourself. You just want someone to blame. Look at those spike marks!" he pointed to my right calf, and I was as surprised as anyone to see the pattern of bloody pinpricks decorating it. I certainly hadn't felt anything during the race.

"Well?" said Skip, to Mick.

He said sullenly, "I thought he tripped me."

"You obviously tangled, but it doesn't look like Cass's fault, now does it?"

Mick stretched out his hand and shook mine.

Mac took Dix's hand and pumped it.

"Good," said Skip, under his breath.

Mr Cootley then came to put in his oar.

"Void race?" he questioned. "Want to race again, or share the prize?"

"He can have the prize," I said. "I won, that's all I'm worried about. Let him have the prize. What is it?"

"I think it's a book," said Cootley, his brow wrinkling in thought. "Yes, I'm almost sure it is. An Agatha Christie novel if I'm not mistaken."

"Christ!" said Mick Gophner, "he can have *that* all right. I give up," and he stalked off, closely followed by his brother.

"Well, that settles that, doesn't it," said Mr Cootley. "Actually, I told a fib. I don't believe it's a book at all. I have an idea that it's a jackknife. I question the wisdom of giving such a prize to schoolboys, but the item was donated by the Navy. It's got one of those spike things on the side, for prising stones out of a horse's gall bladder or something. Come and collect it now, and for heaven's sakes, don't tell Gophner."

I was ecstatic. Old Cootley wasn't so bad after all. He even made jokes about gall bladders. But I was mystified as to why he had lied to the Gophners, and asked him this outright, as we walked back towards the marquee.

"Good Lord, boy, I wouldn't trust a Gophner with blunt cutlery, let alone a Navy jackknife. Heavens no . . . "

So I won my race, got my prize, and stole the heart of a lady.

18

On the evening of 20 June there were more rumours of a massacre. Blue 16 had met some Northumberland Fusiliers passing the cookhouse. The soldiers were in a high state of excitement and anger, saying some of their regiment had been shot down by the Arab Armed Police.

"But they're on our side," protested Del, sitting on the edge of Cass's bed.

"You mean they're *supposed* to be," sneered Blue 16. "Some RCT lads were mown down too, just outside Khormaksar by Arab Federal troops, and three Argyll and Sutherland Highlanders, in Crater . . . "

"Jesus," said Cass. "How many altogether?"

"Somethin' like twenty-three or twenty-four," said Blue 16, "and the terrorists have overrun the whole of Crater. If there's still some lads trapped in there, I don't give much for their chances."

"Well, what was it? Why did they do it? Del's right, they're supposed to be on *our* side. That's what we're staying here for, to secure the place for the Federals. If they're joining up with the terrorists, what the fuck are we doing here?"

Cass had every right to be bewildered. The Armed Police and the Federal Army were the people who were supposed to be taking over from the British after they left Aden. They were the chosen successors of the departing imperialists. Britain was doing its utmost to train these Arabs in the job of policing Aden, so that the NLF and FLOSY could be kept under control when the

Federal Government were given power. Yet these troops and policemen had massacred British servicemen in a cowardly ambush. The RCT soldiers did not even have loaded weapons when they were shot down, because they were passing the barrack huts of their Arab comrades and there was no need to have guns at the ready when in an area protected by friends.

"It was a mutiny," said Blue 16, "that's all anybody knows."

"Shit!" cried Del, punching his pillow. "It's because the bloody gollies lost the Six-Day War, I bet. They're pissed off with Israel, so they take it out on us. Look how they've been going round the last few days, screamin' 'death to the Yahudis' and all that crap. I tell you, if those bastards join up with the NLF we won't stand a bloody chance, man. There's too many of them."

Cass considered this, but he had great faith in the British Army. It was a blind faith, but he believed there was nothing to beat them. He tried to imagine a major confrontation with the NLF and he thought that some of the army lads might even welcome it, since they would at last have their enemy out in the open, instead of skulking down alleys and sidestreets.

Later that evening, Cass went down the hill to chat to Susanne and found to his horror that she had been in an ambulance using the only road from Khormaksar to Steamer Point, and as the vehicle passed the entrance to Crater they were fired upon by terrorists lodged in the fortifications.

"They've got the whole of Crater," she said. "It's a bit frightening to realize we've lost control."

"I thought our lads were killed at Champion Lines – that's at Khormaksar."

"They've got the people that did that shooting."

A surge of justice-at-last went through his veins.

"And what's happened to them?"

Susanne gave him a wry look.

"They've been told off."

"Told off?" Cass exploded. "Told off? For killing blokes in cold blood? What the fuck's going on here, Susanne? What are

190

we, bloody Aunt Sallies, or what? I don't get this. I just don't bloody get it."

"Apparently the Arab soldiers were upset because some of their officers had been suspended, so they mutinied . . . "

"And now they've been given a ticking-off, like schoolboys. *Don't do it again, or you'll get whacked, you naughty boys.* You know what we would get, if we did the same? We'd be bloody shot for it, you know we would. Bloody double-standard bastards. A firing squad for your own kind, but a ticking-off for the other side."

He told the lads when he got back and they were equally incensed at the strange justice handed out by their generals and politicians. They knew, as Cass had said, that if the position had been reversed, the Arabs would be demanding the deaths of the British soldiers responsible. Yet Cass knew, having been raised in this land of dust and rock, that the Federal troops were tribesmen, many of them from upcountry, and had not long since been living wild. Putting them in a uniform and giving them training did not thoroughly tame them. These were men who were used to blood feuds and righting wrongs with a gun, whose idea of justice was to kill the other man before he killed you, because upcountry was a savage place where you watched your back constantly and where every man not of your family was an enemy. Cass knew this, but the English part of his spirit still felt great anger, mostly towards his own kind. So they had taken wildcats and tried to turn them into domestic felines, and the baby had been savaged, its face clawed to ribbons. Did you pat the wildcat on the head and say never mind, it's not your fault, you're a beast of the field? No. You took a gun and you either drove the creature back into the wilderness, or you shot it where it stood.

They should have known, he thought to himself, that you can't domesticate a tribesman overnight. The men from the hills and desert were survivors, and to be a survivor in the wilderness you have to be ruthless and cunning, you have to be first with the gun. That's not something that can be shed overnight, simply

because people from another nation are telling you to be a disciplined force, to act like them, when they've had six hundred
years of practice at giving and obeying orders.

Not only that. Crater had fallen into the hands of terrorists.
There were 80,000 Arabs in the extinct volcano, most of them
civilians, but a good many were terrorists. If they managed to
arm themselves, there could be no security anywhere in Aden.
Surely the authorities would not allow this situation to continue?
They *had* to retake Crater. The volcano dominated the whole of
Aden. Steamer Point was built on its outer slopes. The very billet
in which Cass lived was attached to the side of Crater. The
thickness of a volcanic cone separated his bed from that of a
terrorist. They lived one on either side of a rock wall.

By the time the dead soldiers were buried, a few days later, in
Silent Valley, it had become apparent that the British authorities
were content to let the terrorists keep control of Crater. The
simmering fury of the troops was considered nothing beside the
politics of the situation. Too heavy a hand would bring condemnation from Arabs supposedly loyal to the British and a full-scale
war would erupt. There were Europeans upcountry who would
be entirely vulnerable if a full-scale uprising of the Federal troops
occurred.

The British soldiers had to content themselves with controlling
the situation from the natural rock walls of the enclosed town,
directing fire down on any Arab they saw carrying a gun, or
slipping in, in pairs after dark, with blacked faces, to reconnoitre
the streets. It was not really enough. Not *nearly* enough. They
were human. They wanted revenge for the deaths of their pals.

For the next week, life went on in Steamer Point, Sheik
Othman and Khormaksar as normally as life could in such a
place and at such a time. Cairo radio bragged that the British
were being driven into the sea, that the "bloodsuckers" had been
thrashed and thoroughly beaten by the Arabs of Aden. They
crowed when a British helicopter was shot down over the lip of
Crater and fell inside, though they failed to mention that the

sergeant pilot and his crew fought their way to a safe landing area and were picked up by a Medivac chopper within fifteen minutes.

The tempers of British soldiers were on hold.

Thirteen days after the fall of Crater a folk hero came to the rank and file of the British forces in Aden. He was like most storybook heroes are expected to be, flamboyant and swashbuckling. A young and handsome, clear-eyed lieutenant-colonel, with a cocky air, he looked like Richard Todd and could have played himself in a movie. His superiors disliked him for his showmanship, but he was just what the troops needed, a confident devil-may-care fellow with the courage and audacity of Alexander the Great. Every man jack in uniform below the rank of colonel said fuck the generals and politicians, this is the guy for us. The brass may have thought they could have done without Colonel Colin Mitchell, of the Argyll and Sutherland Highlanders, but Cass knew otherwise.

The rank and file were doing the policing, swallowing the insults, not the authorities in their tall towers, isolated from the streets. It was okay for generals or governors to say, look lads we mustn't rock the boat too much – but for the men in the dust, well they wanted a hero, and by God they had one in Mad Mitch. He even cocked a snook at those who were as much the enemy as the Arabs: the lords in the high castles. One senior officer was heard to remark that "Other commanders were doing *just* as good a job as Lieutenant-Colonel Mitchell, but didn't make such a circus of it." But a circus was precisely what the men wanted. They needed someone with flair, to give them back a sense of pride in the work they had been forced to do. Cass was not in Aden because he chose to be there. He was there against his will. The job was dirty and ugly and there were attacks from liberal people which he would have joined had he been a civilian. Mad Mitch was a glorious banner. Here was a warrior leader who led from the front, as of old, not one who said "Off you go then, boys" from behind. An ugly, dirty job it was, but he did it

193

with firework displays. No more creeping through the streets, waiting for a grenade. No more skulking in doorways. You went in with pipes skirling and the drums beating, and your commander said things like, "We're a very mean lot, we'll be very fair, but if anyone starts any trouble they'll just get their head blown off."

For Cass, a Scotophile since a very young boy, Mad Mitch was perfect: an English-born Scot from Croydon in Surrey.

At the time of the massacre, the Argyll and Sutherland Highlanders had only just arrived in Aden and had never set foot inside Crater. However, their colonel had ensured that they knew every street in the colony before they even saw the brown rocky peninsula of south-west Arabia. He had built models of places like Crater back in the United Kingdom and thoroughly familiarized his men with the landmarks they might expect. He had even given the gymnasium, in which the models stood, a Turkish bath atmosphere, for authenticity.

There were at the very least four hundred armed terrorists inside Crater, perhaps many more. Some of these dissidents were armed with machine guns and automatic rifles, others with bolt-action rifles. They would also have grenades and mortars and perhaps heavier field weapons at their disposal. The generals had prophesied a blood bath, but Mitchell promised them he would retake Crater with the minimum of force, using an understrength battalion of five or six hundred men. To some this appeared to be a foolhardy plan, because traditionally, in order to ensure victory, the attacking force needs to be three times the size of any defending force that has had time to fortify its position. The Argyll and Sutherland Highlanders could barely match the numbers of the defenders. However, Mitchell was a persuasive man, and eventually there was reluctant agreement from the brass.

There are essentially two entrances to Crater, one on the landward side, the other close to the sea. The Argylls refused the offer of another regiment to enter by the main pass, knowing

194

that there was a danger of shooting at each other in the dark once they eventually met. It was safer to enter from the seaward side and roll up the town from one direction. There would be other units, on the ridges above the town, and the main pass would be covered from the outside.

They went in during darkness, with Mad Mitch standing in his Land-Rover and the drums and pipes filling the air with bravado. *Brook us at your peril*, they tattooed. *Stand in our way if you dare*, they wailed. Once inside the pipers played "Monymusk", the Regiment Charge.

Immediately machine guns opened up from the walls of the Sultan's Palace and the soldiers threw themselves to the ground and began to return fire. An armoured car was called up and the fire from this eventually silenced the machine guns, but a single sniper still kept the soldiers pinned down, the shots from this man's rifle ricocheting around in the darkness of the streets. Eventually, the terrorist fire ceased altogether and the regiment moved on.

The Argylls reached the Chartered Bank in the centre of town and established an observation post on its roof. Colonel Mitchell had guessed that most of the terrorists would be concerned about fighting in the dark, whereas his own men were trained for it. He was right, for they met with only token resistance from that point. A force was sent to take Sira Island, attached to Crater by a causeway, and found the enemy had flown. The terrorist banners were torn down and an Argyll flag raised.

The next jobs were to take the Treasury Building and Civil Police Station, both manned by armed Arab police whose loyalty had already shown itself to be in question. The civil police were nervous. They feared punishment for deeds imagined or real. One wrong word or action might have resulted in a bloody battle with the police but a British officer talked them into allowing the soldiers to enter their premises, without a shot being fired.

By the early hours of 4 July, Mitchell was confident of retaking the rest of Crater.

At dawn the inhabitants of the town awoke to the sound of pipes and drums playing from the roof of the Educational Building. Crater was once more in British hands. There had been no blood bath. Only one man was actually killed in the fighting: a member of a terrorist group who attacked a patrol. He was shot dead and his comrades surrendered soon afterwards.

The rank and file had their hero.

When volunteers were called for, to help establish the regiment's positions in Crater, Cass heard himself say, "Me." He was frightened about going into a place which had so recently been in terrorist hands, and was still riddled with them, but for some reason he felt he needed to support the Argylls.

"You're batty," said Blue 16, "you'll lose your bollocks, you will. You're an airman, not a soldier. You're not trained to fight in bloody backstreets."

This worried Cass even more, but when the coach with him and several other lads got there, he found he was to be shifting bags of sand, building emplacements for the Argylls to occupy. As he worked there were Scottish soldiers guarding him. They looked hard and professional and gradually his fears dropped away from him. At one point he caught a glimpse of Colonel Mitchell himself and felt he had something to carry home with him. Later, as he worked, he could sense the resentment of the Arabs watching from the street. He looked up and caught the sullen eyes of one man, and then quickly dipped his head again. The part of him that identified with the adversaries of the British Empire had found its way through to confront the hero worship of the soldiers of the Queen, and caused an internal struggle which was insoluble.

When Cass got back to the billet, he found that incident reports were coming in thick and fast.

"The gollies are tryin' to get their own back," said Del, with

196

satisfaction in his voice. "There's gun battles all over the colony, especially at Sheik Othman."

"They're not *gollies*," said Cass stiffly, once more finding himself torn, protecting his childhood friends against prejudice.

"Aw, fuck, whose side are you on?" snapped Del, his bubble of jubilation having been popped. "I thought you was all for Mad Mitch and his mob?"

"I am – that is, I don't know," said Cass miserably. "I mean, I'm against the terrorists, but all Arabs aren't terrorists, are they? What about Chico, our block-bearer?"

"Listen mate," said Del with narrowed eyes, "Chico has got to stay here after we've gone, and all these other bleeders, and face the bloody persecutions that are going to take place. The closer it gets to departure day, the more jittery he's goin' to get. I wouldn't trust Chico, or the bloke who brings the rooti bread, or old Hassan down there in the shop, any further than I could throw a cathedral. If they can save themselves by cutting your throat, they'll do it – know why? 'Cause you'd do it, if you were in their shoes."

"Some of these people just want to live in peace," said Cass, "I do know that much. Don't call them gollies, Del. I grew up here. I can't stand words like that."

Del flopped back on his bed, obviously offended.

"Suit yourself, mate, they've probably got worse names for us. What's in a name anyway? You got to let out your frustrations somehow, ain't you? Look at the swaddies, doing street patrol. They kick out occasionally, when they've had it up to here, because they get dumped on from all directions. What about this assassin in Steamer? He one of your childhood sweethearts?"

A killer with a Chinese pistol was active in the Crescent, waiting for soft targets, shoppers and business people, before stepping out of the shadows and shooting them at point-blank range through the head.

"That's not fair, Del."

"Life's not fair, mate, or we wouldn't be here, would we? Aw,

197

skip it, you're such a twit sometimes. Bloody hell, golly don't mean anything. My old man called 'em wogs, so did your dad. What does it mean? Nothin', really. Come on, let me buy you a beer." He opened Blue 16's locker with his penknife in a practised move and took a couple of bottles of Amstel from the owner's secret store.

"They're warm, but what the fuck," said Del.

He took the tops off with the same penknife and the beer frothed out. Both men stuck the tops of their bottles in their mouths to catch the foam. Soon they were back to chatting about love, life, and going home.

Cass woke at dawn, with a headache, and watched the sunrise over the heights of Jebel Shamsan. The burnt-sienna craggy shapes looked like prehistoric lizards in the red light: dinosaurs turned to stone. He stared at them, willing them to stretch and yawn, and begin moving over the dust. It seemed to Cass at that moment, as it had done before, that the rocky outcrops were frozen forms of movement, caught in half-action by some magician. Somewhere in time the gulli-gulli man had put a spell on Aden, had petrified a living landscape. Cass could see the faces in the igneous bubbled stone, a look of surprise in their features, to find themselves trapped, locked, at one with the volcano. He and Dix and Heather had played games with those shapes, finding bygone creatures in them, saying that they stalked the desert during the darkness and came back to take their places again once the hard light of the day returned.

The call to prayer came over the rocks and waves, mellow and warming. Out in the harbour the ships were still sleeping. A pi-dog emerged from a hole in the rocks, stretched and shivered out its drowsiness, before having a good scratch and trotting down to the dustbins outside Hassan's shop. On either side of Cass were the lines of sleeping men, some of the beds empty where the owners were on sentry duty. Down below, in the women's barracks, there were one or two lights on, but he didn't get out his binoculars. He had stopped that, now he was going

198

out with Susanne. Not that she would care: she laughed when he told her what he and the boys got up to.

"Bit starved here, aren't they?" was all she said.

Well, he wasn't "starved" any longer. They had made love several times now, and talked away hours, had found each other's strengths and weaknesses, had boasted successes and admitted failures. The good discoveries were delightful, the bad not too awful to bear. It wasn't simply that he liked being with her any longer: he found he could not stay away. Everything he heard and saw seemed to point towards her, and she was in his head from dawn to dusk. He was completely in love with her: the touch, scent, sight, sound, even the taste of her, was now necessary to his existence.

He knew that he wanted to marry Susanne. It was now simply a matter of getting up the courage to ask. He felt sure she would say yes, but he wondered why she never brought the subject up herself. She was an emancipated woman, so it was not feminine reserve that was holding her tongue. He feared that she might have a reason for not wanting to get married, like the idea that marriage was simply a power game. She had spoken of male dominance, and her abhorrence of it. He was afraid that she might be a misogamist. They could live together of course, while they *were* together, though not in Aden. Here, there was nowhere to live except the billets. And when they went back home, they would without doubt be posted to different locations. The Forces do not recognize partnerships, only marriages, so such an arrangement would be impossible for them. After a few months in Britain, Cass would be posted abroad again – that was usual – and he would have to leave her behind. Such an affaire was doomed to be short-lived. It could not survive the length of separations to which it would inevitably be subject.

Someone was up and about, strolling along Telegraph Beach. As Cass watched, he saw the person turning over stones. A shell collector? Cass had scoured that beach when he was twelve years of age. Palaeolithic man had probably combed the same sands

199

for pretty shells to take home to his mate, or even to wear himself, in his shaggy hair, through his nose or ear. In those days no one would call the wearer of such bodily decorations a pansy. No one would sneer at a man for searching and finding beauty in the ripples of the tide.

Some things were eternal, some were transient.

19

For my mother's birthday, I bought her some scent, her favourite, Evening In Paris in a little blue bottle with a silver top. Richie bought her a brass plate with Arabesque designs which could be hung on the wall or used with a tripod as a table. Duggy got her two brass slippers. Dad took her breakfast in bed and his present was a new dress from the Red Sea Shop in Steamer Point. Actually, nearly all the gifts were from him because he gave us extra money towards them. Mum had a cry, partly because she was thirty-three, and partly because we had all remembered this year, with only one or two hints from her. Said joined in the singing of "Happy Birthday to You" but got confused because Duggy's words "*squashed tomatoes and stew, bread and butter in the gutter, happy birthday to you . . .* " threw him off-balance. The rest of us sang the right words. Our Somali cook-bearer thought we were all bonkers anyway, so it didn't much matter.

After the hubbub, I went to church. The Reverend Griffith was in full swing, denouncing Satan and his fallen angels with vehemence. He spoke about a man called Christie who had been hanged recently for killing a lot of women, and offered him as an example of what happened when the Devil got hold of your soul. I was terrified by this, wondering whether I would wake up one morning having murdered lots of people in their beds, because Satan had got into me during the night. I thought hard on what it might feel like to be hanged, perhaps with people cheering and throwing their hats into the air, and it was not a pleasant picture. He then had a go at Jomo Kenyatta, whose name meant "burning-spear", but which the Reverend Griffith thought should mean "burn-in-hell" since he was supposed to be head of the Mau-Mau, who were slaughtering white farmers in Kenya.

He finally wound up with a threat that the world was due for another shake-up, in the form of flood or fire, which the Lord would administer when he thought proper.

It was always hot in the church, this being a low building with poor air circulation, but Rev Griff always seemed to be able to make it feel hotter. Without too much imagination, Aden could be described as a hell on earth, and the padre made the most of that. His eyes blazed and his fists were clenched. His face ran with perspiration and there were dark patches under his arms when he raised his hands to heaven. A large man, he was in danger of losing fingers in the ceiling fans that whirled like helicopter blades above our heads.

"This is the land where Noah's Ark came to rest, on the slopes of Shamsan," he roared, "but not before the whole world, including the mountains, had been covered to a depth of fifteen cubits. Anybody here sixteen cubits tall? No, of course not – no one can stand with his head above the Lord's flood . . . "

"Og did . . . " said a clear young voice.

The padre stopped in mid-sentence and his mouth hung open. I felt an icicle pierce my heart. The person who had interrupted this fire-and-sword preacher, with his booming condemnation of sin and sinners, and his dire warnings of total destruction, was none other than my best friend, Dix. I moved away from him a little, coward that I was, in case the lightning should hit me too, as Rev Griff's eyes roamed the congregation to find the person who had *dared* to interrupt his sermon. Even adults were shifting their feet in anticipation of the storm. The padre scared the living daylights out of the toughest churchgoer. Skip was frowning, in our direction. Heather had her head down, as if she were expecting the worst and didn't want to witness one of her boyfriends perishing in flames.

"Who said that?" cried the Welsh padre.

"I did," said Dix, his head held high.

"What did you say?" thundered the Reverend Griffith.

Dix was never put off by a show of temper from adults. I had seen him quash teachers when he knew he was in the right. His speech did not falter now, as he proceeded to correct God's representative on earth.

"Og, the King of Bashan, according to tradition, walked beside the ark during the flood," said Dix, "so he must have been more than fifteen cubits tall, mustn't he?"

Rev Griff's eyes narrowed.

"Oh must he? Well, how come his bed was only nine cubits long, eh?"

"Maybe his feet stuck out at the end?"

"Don't be daft, boyo. People's feet don't stick out the end of their beds."

"My uncle's do. He's six feet six and he has a chair at the end of his bed to rest his heels on. Maybe Og's carpenters couldn't make a bed long enough for him. After all, one of Og's bones was used to form a bridge after he was dead. A bridge nine cubits long wouldn't be much, would it? Wouldn't be worth talking about, in my opinion. Anyway, his coffin was longer than that. What did he need a coffin bigger than his bed for?"

The congregation was looking from one to another, amazed that the padre was descending to the level of a schoolboy argument. He even looked upset, as if Dix were getting the upper hand.

"Look, be reasonable, young Dickenson. Where did you read this rubbish, anyway?"

"I've got a book on giants. There were two tribes of giants in the Jordan Valley, it says, called the Anakim and Rephaim. Og was one of the second lot, though the tribe had died out by the time he was king, because he lived three thousand years."

"I know about Og, I know about him," cried the exasperated padre. "How do you think I knew about the size of his bed? What I'm saying is, that Genesis doesn't mention him . . . "

203

"Deuteronomy does."

" . . . doesn't mention him walking by the ark."

"Doesn't mean to say he didn't, does it? I mean, what's a cubit anyway?"

The padre, on safe ground, rumbled, "Knuckles to elbow, boyo, knuckles to elbow."

"Quite," said Dix, "I knew that too. Well, the depth of the water in the flood was obviously measured from Noah's arms, which were probably quite small, because people were smaller in those days, weren't they?"

"Yes, but . . . "

"However, the cubits used for Og would've been measured by his own forearm, which was immense, because he was a giant. So one of Og's cubits was worth at least two of Noah's, probably."

"Well . . . "

"So Og's nine cubits would be equal to eighteen of Noah's cubits, even if he was only as long as his bed, and nine Og cubits, which equalled eighteen Noah cubits, was big enough to have your head out of water that was only fifteen Noah cubits deep, wasn't it?"

"I think this has gone far enough," said the padre, evenly.

"So do I," said Dix, "I'm glad you think so. Sorry to interrupt, but I just thought you ought to know."

I heard the words "precocious little brat" hissed from the padre's lips, but no more was said. The Rev Griff carried on the sermon, after a couple of faltering steps. He finished quickly, and with his old strength, cried, "We will now sing 'Rock of Ages', and we will sing it with vigour and feeling, because we *mean* what we sing. The words are powerful, make the voices match the words!"

Everyone groaned quietly. "Rock of Ages". There wasn't a fortnight went by when we didn't sing that hymn. It is a fire-and-brimstone man's hymn. It is a frontier hymn. Whenever a church scene appears in a cowboy film, and the congregation is singing, the hymn will always be "Rock of Ages", never anything else. Catch John Wayne singing "All Things Bright and Beautiful". "Rock of Ages" is the pilgrim's hymn. The settler's hymn. The colonialist's hymn. It is not something sung in a cathedral – that is "Jerusalem", which does well in large hollow stone buildings with a mellow echo – it has to have wooden shiplap walls to flatten its pitch and hard-baked earth surrounds to deaden its notes. It has to be sung with gravel voices, with calloused tones. No castrato would sing "Rock of Ages": it is not a hymn for contralto or soprano. It is the religious fare of the mountain man, the youth with one hand on a gun, the woman who scrubs her clothes by hand with lye soap, the barefoot girl in the gingham dress with the grey lace collar.

Afterwards, as we left the church, instead of kicking Dix's shin, or giving him a left hook to the kidneys, the padre ruffled his hair and smiled, which was a good thing because Rev Griff was almost as big as King Og.

"You know your Bible, young Dickenson. We had quite a sideshow going there, between us, and I think you won."

"I only know bits of it," admitted my friend.

"What bits you know, you have obviously thought about. I like that – but if you interrupt my sermon again, I shall knock your block off." The eyes glittered behind the threat.

"I understand."

"Good. If you want an argument, come to me afterwards. I like a good discussion, especially on my favourite book."

"What book's that sir?" asked Dix, in the voice of an innocent.

"Get away with you, both of you."

The Heather points Dix scored that Sunday were almost without number.

Abdulla met us outside the church. We were going fishing together. Dix wanted to stay home and do something with a model aeroplane he was making. I was never very keen on modelling, I don't know why. I didn't like Meccano much either. I suppose I wasn't cut out to be an engineer.

"How are you, my friend?" said Abdulla, touching me on the

shoulder. Then he gave me one of the fishing-lines he had brought.

"*Tammam. Inta?*"

"Also good," he smiled. "Did you bring the stick?"

I replied in the negative. I had asked Said if he would lend me his African thorn stick, which we knew to be full of magic, to show to Abdulla who was a gulli-gulli man, but the cook-bearer had refused, shaking his head sadly.

"This belong great-grandfather, now belong Said."

He hadn't said any more, but the implication was that it was too precious to let a boy run off with it, perhaps lose it. I appreciated that, although I was disappointed.

We set off for Khormaksar beach. A pi-dog fell in behind us, as if it wanted to join us, but Abdulla kicked out at it, shouting, "*Imshi, imshi burra,*" making it slink away. I had noticed the Arabs had far less tolerance with animals than the British. Left to my own wishes, I would probably have let the beast come along, oblivious of the danger of rabies.

When we got to the *ras* there were several other boys fishing from various rocks, so I suggested we go a bit further round the point. Abdulla agreed, but said we should watch the tide, because it was difficult to get back once the water was high. We scrambled up a chimney in the rock, went along a ledge, then down to a shelf which swilled with water every time a large wave washed in. Once we had crossed the ledge, there were some higher rocks on the other side, and it was here that we settled down to fish.

As usual we were after catfish, and we both had lines with triple hooks. I was still squeamish about baiting them with hermit crabs, so I used cheese and bread-paste, which was almost as good.

Fishing is one of the most pleasant ways to spend one's time in hot weather. You whirl the weighted line around your head like a South American cowboy spins his bolas and then suddenly let fly. There is a swishing sound, then silence, as you wait for the splash a long way out to sea. The *plop* comes, not ever as distant as you want it to be, and then you search for your cork

206

float, bobbing on the surface. Once you find it, your eyes fix on it. Your brain tunes in with the community below the waves, as you will the fish to bite. You settle into a semi-trance, worthy of any Indian mystic. Suddenly the cork trembles. Your body goes electric. The cork trembles again, and again. You jerk the line in excitement! Nothing. The cork begins bobbing again. You can taste the disappointment like salt in your mouth. You curse your impatience for jerking too soon, or perhaps it was too late? Was he about to bite, or had he already taken the bait and was escaping with his prize? Then, while this internal discussion is taking place, *wham*! the cork goes under completely, and the line goes crazy, cutting furrows and circles on the surface of the sea. You begin pulling in, your whole body alive with the moment, your brain pulsing with excitement, your heart running around and barking inside your ribcage, and you hear yourself shouting, "Got one, got one – big! I can feel it – big as a shark!", pulling in, hand over hand, and it does feel big, it feels enormous, and your heart stops running and freezes in motion as you wonder if you'll have the strength (and the courage!) to pull this sea monster from the water, once you get it to the rocks. Maybe it *is* a shark? Maybe it's one of those really ugly fish, all warts and lumps? – a stonefish with deadly poisonous spines? – but the size of a porpoise. Maybe as you pull it out, it'll be so horrific, a Gorgon of the waters, that you'll die of fright there and then? The line zigzags across the top of the water in fury and you pray it doesn't snag itself on rocks, or get caught in weed. And finally, it's there and you haul it up, and though it's not as large as you imagined (for the strength of its fight) it's a pretty big one, oh yes, big as any you've ever caught, sort of a large average, really. The excitement remains for a while, then you settle down again, bait your hook, spin your line . . .

In the meantimes, when you're not actually fishing, you laze around in the sun, watching the dhows out on the water, or the canoe fishermen pulling in their lobster pots. The spray flicks up, fine as a lace veil. A boat goes by, transient rainbows wrapped around its bows. A shoal of small fish, thousands of them, showers into the air and back into the water like silver rain, as something dark and vicious chases them from below. You can see the many-hued coral gardens just below the surface: stag's-head, blue, black, mushroom, brain. Swimming in and out of the hard and soft polyps are the little angels and neon tetras and a hundred other varieties of coral fish. There are jellyfish as large as soup plates, with purple veins and trailing long stingers. There are mean-eyed moray eels and pink-banded snakes. The water is teeming with life, most of it benign, some of it not.

You talk, to pass the time.

"What are you going to do when you are grown up, Abdulla?"

"I have to be a clerk, like my father," he said, the usual smile gone for a moment.

I sat up. "What do you mean, you *have* to be?"

"My father wishes it."

"Well, what do you *want* to be?"

He hung his head a little, his long dark hair flopping over his face. "I don't know. I do not wish to be a clerk, working in the office all day long." His lean hard body seemed to be fashioned for adventure, rather than bookwork. His brown eyes had more depth to them than scribbling required. I really couldn't see him stuck behind an abacus, his fingers flashing the beads back and forth, like the clerks I had seen in the various offices over the colony. Abdulla looked like a boy who would grow into an outdoor man.

"Why don't you ask if you can join the APLs or something – be in the army? You'd be good in the army. You could ride a drom and carry one of those lances."

"I do not like camels," he said with fervour. "I am not Bedu. I wish to drive car, not sit on stinking camels!"

"Well, lots of army people drive cars. You could drive a tank if you wanted."

He smiled at me now, but it was not the old smile.

"I am not tribesman, I am Adeni, born here in Aden. The APL are tribesmen, from the Hadhramaut. Can I join Royal Air Force? Can I fly aeroplane?"

208

I thought about this for a second.

"Well, I've never heard of Arab pilots . . . "

"Ha!" he said scornfully. "So, only white British boys fly aeroplanes."

I protested.

"No, not really. Lots of people do. I expect some Arabs do. I've just never heard of it, that's all. What's the matter with you? You look as if you hate me. What've I said? I only want to help you decide what sort of job you can get."

"I have to be clerk," he said, sullenly, turning back to his fishing. "This is my father's wish. There are no other good jobs for Arab boy from town."

"One day you'll be a big boss, and be able to do as you like."

"Listen, I *never* be big boss," he said. "All big bosses are British persons. Arab only become chief clerk, not manager. Ladies of airmen come new from Britain and say, 'I not want to be housewife here in Aden, my bearer do all housework. I want to be manager of Arab clerks instead.' So British housewife becomes manager of clerks. My father is clerk for seventeen years and still every two years new boss comes, sometimes man sometimes woman, but always have never done the work of clerks before. My father have to show new boss what to do, then go back to scratching books with pen."

"I'm sure there's something else you could do," I suggested, timidly, aware that he was right, that men and women with no experience whatsoever were put in charge of highly-skilled accountants and clerks, simply because they were British.

He nodded, still apparently angry with me.

We fished in silence for a while, then he said, "When I have my wedding, you will come?"

"You bet!" I said, glad we were pals again.

He smiled then. "You are my good friend, Cass."

"Of course I am," I said.

At that moment we were aware of a shark cruising around near our feet. It was a biggish one, around twelve feet long. With

209

dismay, I saw that we had not been taking notice of the tide. Our passage back over the platform of rock was covered with water. I looked behind me, to see if we could climb the cliff, but there was an overhang and I have never been good enough at rock-climbing to conquer my fear of overhangs.

"We're trapped," I said. "Can you shout for a fisherman to get us off?"

Abdulla stood on the highest rock and yelled in Arabic to a canoeist, way out on the water. Finally, the Arab looked up and waved, before paddling off in the opposite direction. By this time the sea was licking at our feet.

"We're just going to have to swim for it," I said. I searched the water for signs of the shark, and found him about twenty yards out, still cruising near the surface. He was probably tracking some fish. I hoped they would lead the creature out to sea.

"We'll have to leave the catfish," I said, indicating our catch. We had about a dozen between us.

"No!" said Abdulla, sharply. "I must take home. My mother waits for these."

There was blood oozing out of the gills of some of them, where we had bashed their heads on the rocks to kill them. The shark would sense us in the water, once we started swimming, come to investigate and find blood . . .

"We *can't* take them!" I reasoned.

"We *must*."

I sighed. My legs were shaking. The shark had dived now, and the sea was washing round our ankles. It was now or never.

"Six each," I said, and he handed me a half-dozen strung out on a piece of fishing-line. I hung them round my neck like a garland, hating the feel of their rubbery whiskers against my flesh. One of them, not quite dead, convulsed, flopping against my breast. Blood smeared my shoulders. It took enormous reserves of courage not to fling the fish out into the sea and be done with them.

"Here we go," I said.

210

I entered the water and gently breaststroked towards the *ras*, which seemed a million miles away. The wind was higher than when we first arrived, and the surface was quite choppy. I tried not to make violent movements, or thrash at all. The sea was remarkably cold and my body shivered. My legs tingled with anticipation, as I imagined at any second those razor teeth shearing me in half. I tried not to think of the woman I had seen taken, just outside the Lido, in water not much deeper than a puddle.

The wind blew the saltwater into my gaping mouth and I kept gagging, swallowing the ocean in gulps. I was aware of Abdulla, just behind me, and could hear his grunting. He was a good swimmer, but fear robs one of energy. I kept my eyes on the point, ahead, where I could see other boys fishing still. They were safe. We were not. Yet.

Something grabbed at my foot, and I yelled, and began racing for the *ras*. I reached it and despite the sharpness of the volcanic rock, was out within a second. I looked down at my foot, fully expecting to see a stump pouring with blood. There was indeed blood, but a relatively small amount, coming from a jagged cut where I had obviously caught my ankle on a submerged rock. There were other, smaller lacerations on my knees, which had been caused by my panic to get out of the water.

I heard a gasping sound behind me, and turned to see Abdulla going under slowly, just a foot from the rocks. I grabbed his long hair and pulled his head up. He caught hold of a projection with his left hand, and I hauled on his right arm. Gradually, he emerged from the sea. He seemed to be whole, without injury. We both stared back, looking for the shark, but the dark waters were free of dorsal fins. Maybe he had gone out into deep ocean long before?

"Thank you," said Abdulla, taking the catfish from me, and he smiled one of his old deep smiles of friendship.

"S'okay," I said, shyly.

The shadow of the British Raj was no longer falling over us.

20

There were pink oleander shrubs all over Sheik Othman Gardens and though they attracted hornets my mother loved them. She was very much a pinky person, when she wanted to be, though she could be dark blue and scarlet as well. This day we were having a picnic and Dix and Heather were with us. Heather's father had heard that he might be going home soon, but none of us kids wanted to think about such a terrible friendless future, so it was usually only mentioned by the adults, though this afternoon was to be an exception. My mother, wise as ever, had threatened me with all sorts of horrible tortures if I dared to stow away on the SS *Devonshire* which was taking Heather away from me. I must admit, it had crossed my mind, and continued to do so until the day she left. Dix and I might have tried it, despite the threats, had not something else intervened between-times, an experience that would take us to the very edge of life.

My mother was using her visitor's voice, because we were entertaining Heather.

"More jam, Heather?"

"No, thank you, Mrs Carson."

I hated bringing my girlfriend and mother to such close quarters. There were all sorts of signals and vibrations in the air, which got into my head, where most of them were probably misinterpreted. I was glad when Dix and I were able to get her away from my parents and walk in the Gardens.

Heather had a blue frock thing on which made her Ayrshire eyes more startling than ever. She did not have an hourglass figure, but she wore all her clothes well. They never looked the wrong size, or out of place, as did so many of the dresses other girls put on. Heather looked just fine. She was Jean, she was Highland Mary, she was Bonnie Lesley. *"For there the bonnie lassie lives, the lassie I lo'e best . . . "* I itched to take her hand, hold it in mine, but I could never work up the courage. Besides, if I had taken her right hand, then Dix would have felt justified in taking her left (even though he was more scared of her than me) and we would have looked silly, three of us walking along, holding hands, looking like a string of human beads. We were much more comfortable, just talking.

During most of our walk though, I sensed that Heather was pensive. She was troubled and it began to worry me. I wondered if her parents thought we were seeing too much of her, or they were fed up with us coming round to her house, or (horror of horrors) if she had fallen for another boy and wanted to be rid of us. This last nightmare was like a foul breath from hell with which I tortured myself deep into long sweaty nights.

"Is everything all right, Heather?" I asked, fearfully.

She gave me a brave little smile.

"Cass, the sensitive one."

"If it's anything to do with anybody we know," said Dix, now aware of her mood, "I'll soon sort 'em out for you."

"Dixie, the protective one."

Suddenly Heather stopped and I was terrified to see that her eyes were wet.

"I'm going to miss you two boys, you know," she said. "Between the two of you, you make as close to the perfect male as I'm ever likely to meet."

"Aw," I said, shuffling my feet. "Don't, Heather . . . "

"I am. I'm going to miss you. I want you to know that, because it's important. Some time . . . some time you'll be glad I told you."

"We'll miss you too, Heather," said Dix, with fervour.

213

"Like blazes, " I said, earnestly. "I just dunno what we'll do with ourselves, honest."

Her face shone again and she dabbed away the tears with her hanky.

"Thanks," she said. "Is there . . . is there anything else you want to tell me?"

Heather, fourteen years, waiting for the words.

Cass, going on fourteen, Dix the same age as Heather, silent, wondering, looking at each other, then away from each other, too afraid to say the words. Why? Well, because . . . because boys didn't say those words and hadn't the adults told us they were not words for children, but for the exclusive use of those who knew what they meant, the grown-up people with all the knowledge?

Heather, waiting to be told she was loved.

Dix and Cass, loving her with all their souls, but unable to tell her how they felt. Cass and Dix, ready to go through fire and flood, to take on life and death, for the sake of Heather.

"No, don't think so," said Dix.

"Not specially," said I. "Leastways . . . no, no, don't think so, Heather."

She tucked an arm under each of ours and held us for a moment.

"Well, I think you do have something to say, but you don't want to say it yet. I understand. You have to save it, for another time, maybe for another girl?"

"Not another girl, never," I cried hotly.

Dix came up behind, red-faced, fierce denial.

"Never another girl."

Her eyes were smiling now.

"Och, that's as good as said, then. Let's talk about something else now. There's still ages to go, before I have to go home to Scotland. I was just teasing you out, you see. Girls have to do that every so often, to find out where they stand."

(Later, I was able to write, "I love you, Heather, I have always

214

loved you, and will forever," but by then we knew we should probably never meet again, and how much more the words would have meant if said on that spell-weaving day with the oleander all around us and the scent of palms to remind us!)

The day at Sheik Othman was a good one. It was one of our last together that was not fraught with other considerations. We went home at sunset, past the saltpans which glittered ghostly white in the dying rays of the day. A BOAC plane roared over our vehicle as we passed the airport to deliver Heather back to her parents, and we watched its lights like a pack of uniform stars falling to earth.

Back at home, the ants were still surging back and forth, red into black, black into red. I had enough imagination to envisage banners and tribal standards, trumpets and bullroarers, drums and fifes, perhaps even bagpipes. I wondered if the same group of ants were always on the front line – the warriors and glory-seekers – while the pacifists and peacelovers remained in the downstairs hall and on the upstairs landing, away from the action. Ants must have had their preferences too. I could not imagine all of them as heroic. Some must have wanted to hunt for food, forage for scraps, lay eggs, look after the young, keep house, laze around in the sun. Surely? Or maybe they all had to take a turn, conscripts, at doing their bit for their country? Maybe there were some ants there, both red and black, who dreamed of going back into the interior and counted the days they spent in boredom and fear on the frontiers of their land?

21

Back in May, the Rolling Stones had been in court on drugs charges. The Beatles were supposed to be swallowing, squirting, snorting and sniffing various substances, mainly LSD. In Vietnam some of the American soldiers were taking mental escape routes from the fighting zone. Their bodies were there, but their minds were in some better place. In Aden there was nothing to be had but *qat*, a grass grown in the Yemen which when chewed for a long time was supposed to clarify the mind and open the channels of perception. A lot of the Arabs used it, walking around with a cheek stuffed with a ball of green silage. Cass tried it once, but it was a laborious business, chewing and chewing, and he felt like a camel. He went back to booze very quickly, getting sorrowful on songs like "Eleanor Rigby". Life went by very slowly, the days on which he was not meeting Susanne like blank cards.

The British forces had been told they were now on "Active Service" which, the warrant officer responsible for discipline explained, "Means sod all to you lot, except that if you get into trouble with me you get double helpings of any punishment that's coming to you." In other words, there were no positive rewards for being in a land which British law recognized as being close to anarchy, but if Cass were to be court martialled for some offence that carried a one-year sentence in military prison, he would receive perhaps two years. The system satisfies itself.

There was a dust storm during the night. Those like Cass and Del, sleeping out on the balcony, woke with the grit in their eyes, noses, mouths, to find their beds and floor, their personal

216

belongings, everything, covered with a thick layer of sand. It took most of the morning to clear it up. At lunchtime, they were able to lie back on their beds and be pestered by the flies, coming in with scorched wings from the direct sunlight. When they could stand the heat no longer they went under the showers, if there was any water, to cool off. Recently the water had been cut off for more hours than it had been available. No one knew why. Shortages (after a flood?). A burst main pipe? The terrorists, perhaps? It was easier to blame the terrorists than anyone else, because they were like an act of God, about which one could do nothing, and therefore there was nothing to do. It was far too hot to go chasing around complaining and getting nowhere with whoever it was that operated the water systems of Aden. So far as Cass knew the authorities were still using the Queen of Sheba's wells, dug in BC days, as reservoirs.

Blue 16 came off his second-to-last sentry duty, crowing, "Days to do!" at Cass and Del.

"We know, we know," groaned Del. "We'll take you out for your gozome tonight."

The rituals: "gozome", the "goes home" party. There Blue 16 would speak of the Happy Bird, the VC-10 passenger plane, that he expected to transport him back to his wife and family, away from the dust storms. There Blue 16 would have his finest hour, getting drunk, singing songs, knowing that he would soon be drinking in the pub back home, and singing the same sorry songs:

> I went to an alehouse I used to fre-quent,
> and told the landlady my money was spent.
> I asked her for credit, she answered me nay,
> for custom like yours I can get any day . . .
> and it's no, nay, never – no, nay, never, no more –
> will I play the wild rover, no, never no more.

Many more, about the Fukawi tribe who were forever asking "where the Fukawi?" and the oomagooli bird who flies low through the trees, crying "oomagoolies" – sad sorry songs that have probably been sung by troops in various ways since Roman legionaries were first stationed in Egypt and Persia and Palestine. The following day Cass and Del would dry him out, stuff him with aspirin and stomach powders, send him out for his last, his very last, sentry duty, and feel sick that it wasn't them on their way home.

"Where are you going now?" asked Cass.

Blue 16 was dressing in civilian clothes, getting ready to go out.

"Bloke's taking me over to Khormaksar, on the back of his motorbike."

"What do you want to go over there for?" asked Del.

"I seen this musical powder compac', in the Naafi, the other day. Gonna buy it for the missus. She'll go ape over it."

Del said, "You've already bought her half of Aden – and your kids the other half. She'll love you for yourself, you know. You can't buy it from her."

Blue 16 looked a little shamefaced.

"Aw, I know. But I want to get it, anyway. It's musical. It plays 'Tulips from Amsterdam'."

"*All* the bloody music boxes in the world play 'Tulips from Amsterdam'," said Cass. "Why don't you come down the Mermaid with us, have an egg banjo on me, and get some panic tanning in?"

"No, no. I want to get this thing."

Once Blue 16 had made up his mind to buy something, nothing would deter him. He was like a stubborn child. He had pictures in his head, of his family standing at the gate, waiting; of him arriving and putting his arms around them; kissing his wife, ushering them all into the house, and there showering them with gifts, watching their eyes sparkle, his wife murmuring, "Thank you, darling," his kids crying, "Cor, *thanks* Dad!", and him, Blue 16 no longer, but now *Darling* and *Dad*, saying, "It plays 'Tulips from Amsterdam', look, I'll show you," and "See, when you press the button the toy dog sits up and begs." Pictures galore, that had kept him going, kept his emotions fed for nearly a year, helped him through the tears and the anger and the frustration and the fear.

"I want to get it," he argued fiercely.

Del shrugged his shoulders at Cass.

"Can't knock the bleeder out, can we? Let's go down the club ourselves, get a couple of bevvies inside us. Looks like another sandstorm's blowin' up anyway."

"Can't," replied Cass, "I'm on duty."

So, they let Blue 16 go.

Cass went on duty after that, first in the watchtower where he sweated away two hours, staring down into the busy streets of Steamer Point. He preferred doing sentry duty at night, rather than in the day, despite the added danger of the darkness. Life was too "normal" during the day. At night he was always on edge, and this kept him sharp for the whole two hours, but while it was light he got lost in the activity in the streets below, and he was wont to daydream. Such dreams were often shattered abruptly, leaving his ears ringing, as an explosion hit some part of the town. He preferred being ready for such noises.

Also, there was the assassin with the Chinese pistol, who was killing so many people along the Crescent these days, slipping out of the shadows, putting a bullet behind an unsuspecting ear, and vanishing into the shadows again. Cass was afraid the man might strike during his watch. Cass did not want the responsibility of a man's death on his conscience. He would feel tremendously guilty, having to say no, if the control room rang him on the field telephone and asked if he had seen anything. No one ever saw the assassin, of course, especially not from any of the watchtowers, even though some of the shootings had been in visible spots. One watcher had seen the body fall, but had not witnessed the actual shooting, and failed to see the killer. The assassin was just another small figure down there among the hundreds in the streets. He did his ugly work quickly and efficiently, and melted

219

back into the crowds. So far as Cass knew, he didn't strike at night.

After watchtower duty, he went into the radio shack and put on his headphones, to begin intercepting Arab broadcasts along with about a dozen other airmen. They scribbled away on the formatted pads, each lost in his own separate world of dits and dahs that, when strung together at blurred speed, made letters, words, phrases, messages containing life and death. Cass could take Morse at thirty-words-per-minute: faster if it was purely figures. At that speed one does not consciously translate the dits and dahs into letters, the subconscious mind has to take over, for instinct can handle such things much faster than thought. The brain heard a sound – dit-dah-dit-dit – and the hand wrote "L", without Cass stopping to consider or even read it. Had he paused at all, to consciously decide upon or read the letter, a dozen other letters would have passed him by before he was able to catch up again. The trick was not to concentrate on what he was doing, but to daydream about other things. This was not just a pleasant frame of mind to reach while one worked, but a necessary state. The work had to be done automatically, unheeded, with a studied lack of attention.

So, diligence to a Morse operator was daydreaming, precisely the sort of thing Cootley had told Cass would get him nowhere in the world. In those far-off schoolboy days, when Cass had spent much of his time gazing out of the classroom window, watching himself rescue Heather from a dozen bandits, or seeing Dix and himself forge new territories through the Amazon, masters and mistresses of the rod had brought him back to the real world with cruel abruptness.

"Daydreaming again, Carson? You stupid boy. How will you ever manage to do a job when you leave school if you spend all your time thinking about things other than the task at hand?"

Well, yah boo and sucks to you. That was precisely what the task in hand required. Cass was regarded as a good operator, because he was able to daydream while he worked. Vigilance and alertness, expounded by Cootley as the prime attributes of a good worker, were not needed. These were required when Cass was off-duty, walking the streets. Cootley had been vigilant and alert at work, catching pupils doing things they shouldn't, and no doubt relaxed when school was over for the day. Cootley was dead, because he daydreamed while shopping in the *suq*.

Cass had at one time despaired of reaching the high state of inattentiveness that wireless operators required. This was back in the days at radio school, as a Boy Entrant airman, at the age of fifteen. He had been signed into the service by his father, on their return from Aden, and had gone to RAF Cosford School of Technical Training, near Wolverhampton. The school had been tough, in more ways than one. The drill instructors and weapons training NCOs had been used to dealing with men, not children, and they did not curb the violence of their tongues simply because their charges were frightened schoolboys far from home. They bore down on them with prison-warder pressure and if a few lads could not stand the strain, well, they went under, they disgraced themselves with tears or by running away. The latter were caught and returned to the camp, where they were actually thrown in jail for the crime of going absent without leave. Jail to a young teenager is an experience which leaves its mark.

Cass was taught to kill at fifteen years of age, with weapons he could hardly lift. He was five feet one inch at the time, and was bullied mercilessly by bigger boys in the senior entries, boys of seventeen and eighteen, whose bodies had matured but whose minds were still caught in the cruelty of adolescent insecurity and underconfidence. Cass and many other boys were beaten and tortured at whim. Once the lights went out in the sleeping quarters and the NCOs went home, the thugs began to roam the corridors looking for victims. There had even been a mock hanging which had almost become a serious accident, though that was investigated by the authorities, who had previously turned a blind eye to mere bruises and broken noses. The humiliation was the worst: being made to do things as if he were an animal.

And in the midst of all this gung-ho activity and ruthless destruction of his personality – all in the name of discipline – he went back into the classroom and learned his trade. He learned teleprinting, Morse, first-line servicing on radio and other devices, mathematics, English, geography, history, telegraphist procedures and all the bureaucratic workings of a military communications centre. There, he almost failed his Morse exams because he wanted to pass them, was diligent, vigilant, alert, and it was only when he relearned to daydream again that he was able to become a good operator, could calibrate radios, take Morse at twenty-words-per-minute, decode pad cyphers. (He was aware, even at the time of learning, that these skills would not last out his working life. They would become a dead language, an anachronism in the age of high technology. Cass was learning how to become a blacksmith in the world of the automobile.)

After eighteen months at the school, they sent him first to an airfield in Norfolk, where he learned to drink beer at the village pub, then to Changi, in Singapore. At seventeen years of age he was thrown into the heady delights of the Far East. There had been few postings since which he had enjoyed as much as Singapore. Not even the coral island in the middle of the Indian Ocean. Not even Nairobi. Certainly not Aden.

Cass's hand wrote furiously, the message appearing before his unseeing eyes as just marks on a piece of paper. It could have been Sanskrit for all he knew during the taking. Only when the broadcast stopped did he come out of his trance and actually read what had bypassed his conscious mind, what he had written with those fingers calloused by several years of doing the same thing.

222

He left the radio shack at noon, passing Flight Lieutenant Parkinson on the way out, who nodded to him.

"Corporal Carson."

"Sir." Cass saluted the officer.

"We're closing in."

"Sir?"

"You know who I'm talking about. Your pal. I might need you soon."

Abdulla Achmed. The gulli-gulli man.

Cass's heart sank.

In the afternoon he, Del and Susanne went to the Mermaid. They played a game with rusty old cargo vessels that passed in range of their binoculars. Many of these freighters had missing letters from the front of their names, where the continual washing of the bow waves had worn them away, often leaving the last three or four letters further back along the hull. ON STAR, on an Indian ship, had no doubt been RANGOON STAR, at some time. The idea was to think up the most outrageous name which would fit in with the letters which were left, though the real name could often be verified on the stern of the ship, once it had passed by.

"A-R-D," said Cass, letting the binoculars fall to the extent of their straps.

"MUSTARD," cried Susanne.

"CUSTARD," said Cass.

"BASTARD," crowed Del.

The winner of that round was of course Del.

It was a silly game, but they were into trivial pastimes, since serious matters were unwanted yet omnipresent. Cass maintained that the Noah's Ark had not been called the Ark at all, but the Skylark, only when the time came for recording the name, it had already made its famous voyage and stood weathered and beaten on the slopes of Jebel Shamsan.

Cass explained, "When Noah went round calling the animals

223

in, incidentally, fourteen by fourteen in most cases, not two by two, he shouted, '*All aboard for the Skylark!*' "

"Well, that makes sense to me," said Del.

And Susanne simply laughed.

They stayed at the Mermaid Club, for that was the venue of Blue 16's gozome. When evening-time came around and laid its purple bars across the waters of the Indian Ocean, they left the beach for the clubrooms. There were already one or two drinking parties in progress, probably celebrating nothing but the successful end of another day. There the trio waited for the arrival of Blue 16 and several other people.

Gradually friends and neighbours began to trickle in, but no Blue 16 appeared on the horizon. By eight o'clock, Del was saying disgustedly, "He's probably still over at Khormaksar, pissed out of his brains. I bet the bugger's rat-arsed: met someone at the Naafi bar over there . . . "

"He wouldn't do that," said Cass. "*You* would. Maybe *I* would, but not Bluey."

"Don't you believe it, mate," said Del. "Blue's a little goer on the quiet."

So they continued waiting, drinking steadily. The party at the next table was in full swing and despite the presence of one or two women, drunks were doing the "Zulu Warrior", standing on tables and pulling off their clothes to the song, "*Haul 'em down, you Zulu warrior, haul 'em down, you Zulu chief, chief, chief, chief, chief . . . *" Some steam-headed sailor tried to persuade Susanne that she would be better off with some "real men" until Del stood up and persuaded the rating that she was already in the company of such creatures.

"Bloody matelots," snarled Del.

"Fuckin' crabfats," sneered the sailor.

Fortunately the affair went no further than threats and stances, because Susanne told them both to sit down and behave themselves, and Cass stepped between them, saying to the sailor, "For

Christsakes pal, we're here on a gozome. Come back tomorrow morning at six and we'll sort you out then."

The sailor went, saying "he would be there" which everyone knew was a lie, just as Del and Cass intended to be nowhere but in their beds at six in the morning. They carried on drinking, waiting for the appearance of the guest of honour, thinking that perhaps he was going to come dressed as a cockerel or something outlandish, just for a few laughs.

At half past eight someone came up behind Cass and whispered in his ear.

"What?" He whirled, to find himself facing one of Blue 16's fellow cooks. The man was pale and nervous.

"S'Blue. He's dead," repeated the man.

The whole bar went silent. Even the sailor who had wanted female companionship stopped yelling the odds with his mates, and stood there with a half-sober look on his face.

"Dead? Blue? What happened?" said Del.

"They was on a motorbike, him and another bloke. Both got it. Stopped for petrol at that garage, halfway to Khormaksar, and some sod came out of the backstreets and sprayed 'em with a machine pistol. Sorry, Del, sorry, Cass. I know he was your mate. That's why I came to tell you. Just walked up behind them and let them have the whole mag-full. Didn't stand a chance."

"Siddown, have a drink," said Del, automatically. "Take the weight off, take – it – off . . . " His eyes were glazed and he stared at the tabletop. The cook, still in his stained whites, dropped down into a rattan chair and picked up an opened bottle of beer. He had guzzled half of it down before Cass spoke again.

"Shit! Those *bloody* bastards."

Susanne put her hand on his arm. The sailor wandered over, saying, "Couldn't help hearin' that. Sorry about your mate. Heard it on the incident report this afternoon. Didn't know you knew him then, o' course."

"This was his gozome," said Del. "This was Blue's goin' away party."

"Jeez, I'm sorry, mate . . . "

Del looked shaken. He grabbed a bottle of whisky from the little stand of spirits in the middle of the table, opened it, and drank straight from the neck. Cass got up and stumbled out of the doorway and down to the beach. He stood there looking at the waves. Susanne came up behind him, but stayed a few yards away, watching him. Then she said, "It's all right, Cass."

He looked round at her. "What's all right?"

"I know what you're thinking, and it's all right. It's natural. Del's thinking the same thing too, and feeling the same guilt, but he drowns it in alcohol."

"What am I thinking?"

"You're feeling bad because the first thing you felt was a sense of relief – that it wasn't you."

He said nastily, "How come you know so much about it?"

She came and stood before him, ignoring the malicious tone.

"Because I felt the same thing. We all liked Blue, but we have this survival instinct, which seems to work against the flow of our emotions. It doesn't mean we're not upset because he's been killed. We feel two things, that's all – glad and sorry – side by side."

He suddenly collapsed inside, the supports all gone.

"But what if it had been you, Susanne? What if – if you had been killed and I felt that way? That's a terrible thing. That's a terrible thing . . . because I love you, don't you see."

"I love you too, Cass, so it wouldn't matter, would it?"

He stood there, swaying for a moment, the sorrow welling up inside him. Then he fell into her arms and suddenly he was not afraid to cry. The tears came streaming down his face as they hugged each other hard.

"He was such a pathetic bloke," said Cass, when he could catch his breath, "such a soft little bugger. What did they want to go and kill *him* for? All he ever wanted to do was get home to his wife and kids."

A moment later, they were interrupted, as Del came staggering out of the club and was violently sick into the sand. They each had their own way of dealing with their grief. Cass knew why Del was trying to get drunk. The pair of them had to go back and face the empty bed on the balcony, the locker full of toys and gifts for a family that would never see husband or father again, and the chuff chart pinned to the wall which said: DAYS TO DO ARE GETTING FEW.

22

Skip helped with the planning of The Journey, the last task we had to undertake in order for Dix and me to get our scout's First Class badge. Once we had the First Class under our belts, we were both well on the way, myself towards a Bushman's Thong, and Dix his Queen's Scout. We already had several of the extra badges required for both these coveted awards.

"Now, it's essential you keep a good diary," said Skip, as we sat drinking cocoa in the scout hut, "because the Commissioner will require that as evidence that your time was well spent. Remember to record all your observations on your walk. If we were in Britain, you'd be noting trees and flowers, that sort of thing, but out here you'll probably not see a great deal of flora. There'll be the odd shrub or two, and desert plant. I suggest those you don't know the names of, you draw, well enough for someone to recognize what they are. You'll probably see a bit of wildlife, which will be interesting. Make an entry at least once an hour, with the time in the margin. Don't be frightened to put your *feelings* down on paper. This is life experience. Throw in a few emotions, opinions, that sort of thing. It's not an exam. There's no right and wrong way, or answers, just a document which tells us what you did, how you felt about it, what your thoughts were, that sort of thing. Got it?"

We nodded. Neither of us were any great shakes at writing down our feelings and thoughts, but we were desperate to get the badge, so we were jolly well going to have to try.

The Journey was to take place the next weekend. It would

begin on Friday morning and end Sunday morning. We had been given maps of the area and were expected to stick to the coastline, travelling first north, then north-east as the coast curved round. We would be met on Friday and Saturday evenings, not to be helped, but simply because we were venturing out a little beyond civilization. Skip and a couple of other scouters would camp nearby, to keep us company in the wilderness.

"Remember to stay with the shoreline, and you won't get lost," reminded Skip. "We'll be keeping an eye on you, anyway."

My mother was not too happy about the whole affair, and I kept telling her that it wouldn't kill me, and to stop her fretting.

"Dinna fash yersel', woman," I told her in my best Scots accent, trying to jolly her into not worrying.

It didn't do any good, of course, telling her not to get anxious. Mum was a wraith of a lady, simply because she enjoyed fretting and fussing over us. No diets were necessary for our mother, who had never weighed more than seven stone in her life, and was much of the time between hovering around the six mark. She was a furious little woman who burned her way through the business of living, like a fast-fizzing fuse.

Said was also anxious.

"Many bad man out there," he said, shaking his great ebony brow, "you better be stay here."

The elderly African looked on himself as an extra father to us now and was always giving us advice. He still chatted to me about his relatives, in Somaliland, and regaled me with long descriptions of the village life over there, which seemed remarkably sordid. I had no difficulty in imagining him as a child running barefoot amongst scrawny chickens and flea-bitten dogs, sleeping on dirt floors with the jiggers, and walking thirty miles to school each day. He was such a dignified person that I realized he must have been a tearaway, full of effervescence, as a boy. A man like Said could not have been so gracious all his life: he must have been a convert to mannerly behaviour. Not because he was a black African. I knew several of his countrymen who one instinctively realized had been staid and formal all their lives. No, Said must have attained his dignity, rather than grown with it, because he wore it like a new cloak. I liked that idea, that he had once been a desperado. It suited my mental picture of him and it explained his occasional wicked grins, which I supposed was him remembering some awful deed he had perpetrated in his youth.

"Can't stay here, Said," I told him. "You'll have to do some magic, to keep me safe."

He drew himself up.

"Said not *witch doctor*. Said *Moslem*."

"Well, can't you be a Moslem and do magic as well? My friend Abdulla does magic, and he's a Moslem."

However, Said declined to dance around the garden naked late at night, or burn some foul root in order that I come back whole, or even crush a few scorpions under a full moon. He said he would pray for my safe return, and I had to be satisfied with that. He did too, because I heard him.

Heather said she knew we would do well, because we were resourceful boys. We were Heather's boys, life and soul. We were to go out into the wilderness, wrapped in Heather's love, under the protection of Said's prayers, and guarded by my mother's worry-thoughts. What harm could come to us with such an array of angels warding off the evil that men and deserts do?

Dad helped me pack my things. It wasn't often he got excited about something any of us boys did, but somehow going out into the desert had caught his imagination. He said he knew what to pack because he often went upcountry on exercise and no doubt I had to take the same kind of things. The only trouble was, once we started to round up utensils like tin openers and flasks, Dad realized it was Mum who packed for him because she was the only one who knew where all the items were hidden in the house. So in the end we called on her to help us and though she grumbled that "men" didn't know their knee from their elbow, it was obvious she enjoyed being indispensable.

230

That week school dragged. I had come to like school enough to be tolerant of sitting at a desk for two hours at a time, but when there was a future promise on the wind it was different. My legs twitched the whole time and I longed to be up and away. I watched the dromedaries slapping along the main road with their pancake feet, pulling watercarts or loads of *qat*, or simply carrying a man. Camels did not walk, as such, they did a kind of galumphing slip-slapping dance which invited merriment, but at the same time possessed a kind of haughtiness which eventually turned that laughter against the mocker. Camels do not take kindly to joshing, either, if they can get their teeth within reach of human flesh.

Being a main highway, the road outside the school carried all the traffic, including pedestrians, from Sheik Othman to Crater and Steamer Point. In those days many people did not ride, either on an animal or in a car, but walked from place to place. A constant flow of barefoot travellers passed by our windows, the curious ones amongst them peering in occasionally. They all had names, of course – very fine religious names – but to the British troops guarding the camp they were "John" or, if clearly young boys, "Chico". "Where are you goin', John? Got some stuff for the cookhouse, 'ave you? All right, on yer way then." " 'Ello Chico, where you think you're off to then? Can't come in 'ere, lad, this is military property . . . " John. Chico. Choki. I had the sense at that age to wonder whether the locals resented this general wiping away of individual identities. I also wondered whether they had a name for us and suspect they must have done. Abdulla denied this and so did Said, but I'm sure there was an Arab word which covered the sprawling mass of pink intruders from across the sea. Probably not a very nice word, if they had any sense of humour at all.

The end of the week crawled closer.

Ma Gower, as we had come to call her, moved amongst us with bovine majesty, correcting, mildly admonishing and giving us of her teaching as generously as Audhumla gave of her four

231

rivers of milk when she nourished the Norse giant, Ymir. We were her cherished charges, suckled educationally by this large and heavy goddess of the cud. She filled us with learning, until we were fit to burst, and it was full-cream learning: Browning, Dickinson, Byron, Keats, Wordsworth, Coleridge, Tennyson, Yeats, the Brontës, Jane Austen, and ancient history and classical mythology, sprinkled lightly with just a pinch of mathematics, and a dash of geometry and science, but nothing too spicy to spoil the richness of the prime succour. Ma Gower thought it more important that we knew that Byron's favourite dog was called Boatswain, than discovering that x can equal $3\frac{1}{2}$ in given circumstances. After all Boatswain was a constant, whereas x was a fickle thing, chopping and changing.

Cootley, on the other hand, saw mathematics and science as the protein we needed to redden our corpuscles. What Ma Gower missed in her enthusiasm to bloat us with poetry and literature, Cootley stuffed into us on the occasions he got his hands on us. We swallowed mouthfuls of amino formulae in his presence and either choked on them or held them down and allowed them to fill our bloodstreams with russet hues. Cootley was an old-fashioned teacher, a stalker and pouncer, who rammed things down your throat like a fox feeding its young with regurgitated meat.

Finally Friday came and Dix and I rushed to our homes to get kitted out ready for The Journey. Mum helped me on with my backpack (Dad's service webbing backpack actually, with brass buckles that shone like new gold) and loaded me down with extra food which I knew would cause Skip to throw a fit when he saw it. I then trudged off to see Dix and we wrote the first entry in our cardboard-covered exercise book:

> *1317 hours.   Kitted up and ready to hike. First stop the*
> *scout hut. Saw a pi-dog on the way.*

When we got to the scout hut, Skip inspected our packs and

then we were bundled into a vehicle which drove us out to the beach opposite Sheik Othman, on the east coast.

Skip pointed north-eastwards.

"That way, gentlemen," he said, "and good luck. We'll see you this evening, round about six o'clock."

We saluted our best three-fingered salute, and feeling like a pair of Rudyard Kipling's Kims, we set forth along the shoreline, pausing only to enter things in our diary. To our right was the sea and to our left the desert – two vast areas of nothingness – while ahead was a line that passed between them known as the shoreline. As we walked, we sang our favourite scout songs:

I used to be a Boy Scout and a jolly good Boy Scout too,
but now I've finished my boy scouting I don't know what to do.
I'm growing old and feeble and I can't Boy Scout no more,
so I'm going to get my ticket if I can – back to Gilwell, happy
*   land,*
and I'm going to get my ticket if I can.

Or less serious:

Oh, they say that in the Boy Scouts, the food is mighty fine –
a bun fell off a table and killed a pal of mine...

Songs to keep the feet moving, to keep the heart light, to remember Lord B-P and Mafeking by. Scouting was, for me, woodsmoke, burned baked beans, canvas roofs, staves, ropes, knots, first aid, paddle your own canoe, and:

Remember 'bout de possum, sitting on de limb,
wid de gun a pointin' at him and de dawgs a tree-in' him,
how he holler to de hunter and he holler to de hound,
I'se goin' to keep a grinnin', though I spec you'll fetch me
*   down.'*

Catchphrases: *one thousand volts, two thousand volts, three thousand volts – SHOCKING – three thousand volts, two thousand volts, one thousand volts – REVOLTING.* It was splices, crown knots, rope-

233

lashings, bridges of staves, wide games, neckerchiefs, leather Gilwell woggles, maps, compasses, finding your way in the wilderness . . .

23

Tragedy often occurs as the result of a series of errors and circumstances, any one of which might be overcome on its own, but which clustered together bring disaster. The compass had been fixed by a small brass ring to Dix's belt, from which he had a number of items dangling, including his tin cocoa mug. When we stopped to take a map reference, however, and he reached for the instrument, he found only the ring. The compass case and its contents had become detached and lay somewhere back along the trail. We shrugged our shoulders at this unfortunate loss, but decided to continue The Journey, since we really did not need a compass to follow the coastline. Or so we thought.

As the walk progressed, the meandering shoreline became less accessible to the traveller. We had begun on the sandy beach itself, but due to the frequency of rocky headlands and deep inlets, were gradually forced inland. It seemed silly to walk out on to a promontory, simply to walk back again and get no further than a hundred yards. So we began cutting across country from one fiord to another. Gradually, these inlets got further and further apart, until we were starting out for a point which was not visible, thinking we were walking in a straight line. Since we had no compass it was inevitable that we misjudged, and found ourselves out in the desert, no doubt having taken a line directly north instead of north-east.

Still, we did not get overanxious, thinking all we needed to do was cut directly east and we would be bound to reach the sea again, eventually. There was an enormous ocean in that direction, which the whole coastline followed until the Gulf. We could surely do it with our eyes closed.

The theory still holds good, as I stare at a map of the region while writing this account, and I still do not see how we failed to find the ocean, but the fact is, we lost ourselves in the wilderness. Maybe we went round in circles, or spirals, or curved away from the ocean every time we neared its shores. Any one of these looks feasible on paper, when you see the vastness of the landscape covered by the wasteland. We were two resourceful youths, with some training in pathfinding, but the desert is a mighty place. It is the King of Solitude. Amongst wildernesses, it is a giant. Whole armies have lost themselves in smaller deserts than the Hadhramaut, let alone two young boys. If we were truly heading north, we could have walked for months and seen not a sign of human life – except, of course, without water one would die within a few days.

At four o'clock we should have been nearing our destination somewhere along the shore, where the scouters would be waiting for us. The sea should have been to our left and the desert to our right. In fact we had a sea of gravel on one side and a sand-and-rock terrain on the other. I couldn't even *smell* the ocean, and neither could Dix. That we were in grave trouble came as a gradual realization.

"We're lost," I said.

Dix nodded. "How much water have you got?"

I shook the water-bottle my dad had let me borrow.

"Quarter of a pint," I said.

"Me too. We've been drinkin' too much."

"Well, we thought we'd be with Skip by now, didn't we? Anyway, it's too late for worrying about what's been drunk. We've got to eke out what's left, until they find us."

We looked at the horizon. All around us was wasteland, with little shade. Dust swirls were born and died in the burning air and the heat came out of the ground as if it were generated in hell. We were getting it from both above and below. There were

236

no sea breezes to move the heavy atmosphere, nor could we hear the sound of waves. Any plants we could see were crisp, like crumpled brown paper, struggling for life amongst gravel. A sky as hard as blue slate pressed down on our heads. I was hot and tired, the dust mixing with my sweat and making my joints sore. I wiped my arm over my forehead and the grit that had stuck there was like sandpaper scratching my skin. My eyes were watering from too much sun and there was a pain in the base of my skull.

"Shall we wait here, till they come looking?" I said. In all the books I had ever read on survival, they told you to stay where you were, and be found. Yet that was usually by some crashed aircraft, or in a place others knew you to be. In our case, we were well off-track, and there was nowhere to rest in the shade. When I looked in any direction, I could see a forever of nothing. The landscape seemed to be formed only of waste material: the bits of useless rock and dust left over after God had made the world. It was as if the Creator had given up on this piece of the earth, as a farmer will despair over a field of chalk and flints, and had worked his agricultural wonders around it, leaving it barren.

I felt as tired and empty as the desert around me. I could not imagine there being any people in this place. It looked as though no one had been here since Genesis. Our Welsh padre could have used it as an example of what hell would be like. There was no spirit in it that had not withered from waiting. There were no ghosts that had not long since dried up and blown away. Even the wind had no direction, no real identity. It was born amongst the dismal stones and died there, a *gamin* wind, a wind with no pedigree.

Dix looked just as exhausted as I felt. His face was grey and his cheeks sagged. I had never seen him look so defeated and it frightened me. Dix was always the strong one, the hero of the match, the rugged British boy with a long tradition of stiff-upper-lips behind him.

"I dunno," he rasped, sounding as if his throat were choked with dry thistles. "They'll go south-west along the shoreline first, won't they, thinking we're just slow?"

He was right.

"I suppose so. I guess if we keep walking the right way, we'll come to the water again."

"Yeah, but we don't know the right way. I've been using my wristwatch hands, the way we was taught, but it's all a bit vague. I mean, the sun's over there, right? But it's big, and where exactly do you aim the hour hand? You can't look, it's too bright, and it only has to be off a fraction and we're probably pointin' in the wrong direction."

We sat down and rested near a clump of rocks, wary of snakes and scorpions. We saw only a lizard, its breast pulsing, inching its soft belly over a stone that would have burned our fingers to touch. It regarded us suspiciously with tiny darting eyes, then it slipped into a crack in the stones. After a while I felt myself dozing. I shook myself awake. I was already feeling thirsty and we had to guess on spending a whole night without any further water being available to us. I don't think I was so much frightened about dying, though that was a distinct possibility, as I was anxious not to be thirsty. There is a difference between these two. Death was a distant fear, but thirst was an immediate concern.

If we could find the coast again, there would be no problem in getting water. I knew from my survival training that all one had to do was dig above the high-tide mark to find the fresh water that flows under the land and down to the sea. It is usually only a few feet below the surface at that point, and sand is easy to shift. If we could have found the beach, we would only need to wait there for rescue.

In those days we carried no polythene bags or sheets, so we could not get water by condensing the moisture from the air. We did have a mirror, which we dangled from the tip of one of our staves, so that its flashing could be seen from a much further distance than our forms would be visible. Although we were extremely hot in our thick scout shirts we remembered to keep them on, so that our perspiration would not condense as quickly as it would have done if we went down to skin. We tried to make ourselves some sort of tent, out of the clothing we carried in our packs, to give us some shade.

Dix had a set of dominoes in his bag and we cleared a space on the sand and began to play to keep our minds off our predicament. Although nothing had been said, I think we both realized we would have to wait until dark to travel any further. We could use our torches once it got dark, which would replace the mirror on the stave for long-distance signals. If they were out looking for us, they would certainly follow up any flash of light, however remote the chance that it would be us.

The last couple of hours of sunlight seemed to make the desert warmer, not cooler, but then once the light had gone the temperature dropped dramatically. We were not used to this, on the coast, where the nights were almost as hot as the days. It began to get distinctly chilly and we both put on jumpers to keep warm. We allowed ourselves a cup of water, since our throats were parched by this time, and though it might have been psychological, Dix complained of dizziness.

Creatures began to come out from their daytime hidey-holes now, and we could hear them making noises amongst the shale and other loose rocks. They might have been as big as snakes or as small as spiders for all we knew, but we did know that most creatures out in the desert were not particularly endearing. I had no wish to meet horned vipers or puff adders, or any snakes for that matter. Scorpions and spiders could be stepped on, but a cobra was not so easily removed from the world. The trouble was, in the darkness skinks and other lizards could easily be mistaken for snakes, and we were constantly jumping this way and that, thinking a deadly set of fangs was only a few inches away.

We lit a fire to keep the demons at bay and as a signal to anyone who was out looking for us. The plan was to try to sleep the first part of the night, then to begin walking around midnight. Neither of us was anxious to get up and go, since we had only a vague idea of the direction to take. We had found the Plough in the sky and from that the direction of the North Star (though it was hidden in a haze of light cloud on the horizon), so we knew roughly which way to point our bodies and set our feet going. However, our experience had told us that we were good at going slightly wrong, and that *slightly* was a major factor in our getting lost.

We sat and stared into the flames, our thirst still there but not raging, as it had been during the day. We had gathered as much grass and bracken as we could before the sun went down, but the fire would not last long after sunset, unless we burned some clothes or the staves, which we were not inclined to do at that time. It was bright while it lasted and we made the most of it, using it as somewhere to rest our gaze while we opened up our hearts to each other.

Dix said candidly, "I could've killed you once, when I was trying to get Heather for a girlfriend and you came and butted in."

I felt guilty. I couldn't dispute his words.

"I'm sorry," I said, "but I didn't know I liked her until you said you did."

"Maybe you liked her *because* I did?"

"Might have started out like that," I admitted, "but now I'm nutty about her and I'm not going to walk off just because you decided you liked her first."

"Don't expect you to, not now," he said, his round glasses glinting in the firelight, "but I still could've killed you."

"I don't blame you for that. I could kill you sometimes, when you and her get together over that classical music and start taking the mickey out of me for liking Eddie Cantor."

"You could kill both of us I expect," he said, acknowledging for the first time that it was indeed a conspiracy.

"No," I said, "just you."

240

This made him look at me through the flames, but he shrugged, possibly realizing I could do nothing to hurt Heather, even if she murdered my mum and dad, burned my favourite books and ran off with Bags Williams to a faraway place. Heather was to be loved, whatever her future faults, and nothing else, nothing less. It was adult love that turned to hate, mixed as it was with passion. We owned the purity, the essence of what later became tainted with strong and urgent, but destructive, feelings like jealousy, anger, fear.

If I think casually what I would feel on being lost in the desert at night, I am sure to imagine fear of the unknown as part of the experience. When I look back clearly, however, I can say that it was not. When I try hard enough, I remember I was not afraid of anything supernatural out there, no wild imaginings or nightmarish thoughts came to me. It is not the darkness of outdoors that troubles me, but the darkness of houses, the corners of old rooms. I think smell has got a lot to do with fear. There is a definite smell to supernatural evil. Ghosts carry an odour, whether they exist or not. By that I mean, even if the monster in the wardrobe, or under the bed, is merely imagined, the brain plays tricks with the olfactory sense and we have visions of smell, just as we hear and see things that are not really there. The desert just smelled of earth and rock.

We found bits of stuff to keep the fire going for a while, using our torches, but eventually it died on us. Once it was out we came to realize that the night was quite bright, with a heaven full of stars, and we did not really need the torches or firelight to see our way. We needed to preserve the torch batteries in any case, so that we could signal every so often, in each direction.

At midnight, we started walking in what we thought to be the right path. We had to move slowly, for though it was a bright night, there was still the danger of tripping over a rock and injuring ourselves so that we could not walk. That indeed was a scary thought and we moved quite cautiously.

After a while, walking becomes a mind-numbing experience,

whereby one foot is placed before the other and no more thought goes into the action. We shuffled along, going we hoped towards the coast, only occasionally encouraging one another with ideas of rescue. All I could think of at that time was getting my lips around the neck of a cold bottle of lemonade. The image of that icy bottle, the condensation running down the outside, wetting the label, became an obsession.

About an hour after we had begun walking we heard the sound of an aircraft, possibly a helicopter, somewhere behind us. We turned and yelled, but it was a pathetic attempt. The noise of the engine told us they were not close and even had they been right over us they would never have heard us. Only when the sound was fading away did we remember to flash the torches. Belatedly we tied one to a staff and held it up, waggling the end, but the sound of the engine never returned. We waited for about half an hour before heading on, a little cheered by the prospect that they were out looking for us. They would never have sent up an aircraft at night otherwise. We knew that much.

In a few short hours, Aden, the place that had meant security and warmth and love to me, had become a threatening dangerous land which might be responsible for my death within the *next* few hours. It was as if we had found the lioness that was mother to the cub: we had played with the tame baby Aden for almost two years and now we were dealing with the adult. Out here in the desert there were wild tribesmen who thought nothing of killing strangers. We were youths, not adults, but would that save us? We did not want to put it to the test. We had heard the horror stories of the picnic parties that had strayed into the wrong areas and ended up having their heads displayed on poles, or simply left to rot in the desert, stripped clean of their clothes. There were colonials in Aden who thought the desert Arabs wouldn't harm flies. There were others who believed them to be noble creatures who upheld the laws of hospitality as outlined in their culture and in their religion. There were those who believed tribesmen to be all bandits and brigands who would cut your throat as soon as spit. The truth was somewhere between these extremes. There were good and bad people out in the desert, just as there were good and bad people in a city: the problem lay in recognizing which was which. Since we were completely ignorant of the desert and its people, it was best (we thought) not to attract the attention of any tribesman who had not seen us, even though we might have been given water if that person was hospitable.

We trudged on until dawn, taking sips of water here and there, and wondering if there would be dew on the plants that we could lick to supplement our rations. When the sun came up, hot and dusty from its escapades below the horizon, we had decided to open a can of beans and drink the juice. We also had a tin of Campbell's soup, but it was of the solid variety, which needed water with it. The beans were a good idea, since they provided breakfast, though the juice was not at all as thirst-quenching as we believed it would be. Once that was gone, we had a tiny bit of water left. It was essential that someone found us that day, or that we reached the coast.

By ten o'clock, we were in some rocks, trying to keep under shade, while the fire-ringed sun above us seemed intent on burning our brains out of our skulls. No breezes stirred the dust and the haze that accompanied heat hung over the land, distorting images and providing us with mirages. Our tongues began to feel uncomfortable in our mouths, as if they were dry-swollen and rough. I had a raging headache and my eyes hurt, while Dix complained that he wanted to go to the toilet but nothing would come out. The temperature, at a guess, was well over 100 degrees Fahrenheit. The sweat was soaking our clothes and evaporating. Skip had told us the human body needed three to four pints of water a day under normal conditions. In the desert lost fluid had to be replaced rapidly and the intake of water had to be a lot higher than normal if we were to stay alive, due to the swiftness of the loss.

We had but a dribble of water left in our flasks.

243

24

"You're married," Cass said, the words sounding leaden even to his own ears.

Susanne clung to him, tightly.

"I never thought it would get this serious. Cass, I've written to him. I've asked for a divorce. We were as good as separated anyway. I love you, Cass," she was crying now, "I don't want to lose you. Oh, God, I feel sick. *Why* didn't I tell you before?"

"Married," he repeated. He wanted to throw her from him, so that he could think properly. His mind was spinning and she was making it worse, clinging to him like a baby monkey to its mother. He needed to *think*.

"I'm sorry," she whispered. "I'm so sorry."

They were standing outside her room, and she had told him impulsively, just as she was saying goodnight. She had blurted it out, as if it had been stuck in her throat all evening, and she couldn't keep it back any longer. Perhaps she had been trying to say something for days, but had been unable to find the right time, get it together?

She kissed him several times on the cheeks and eyelids.

"I tried to tell you, but I was scared. I thought it would turn you away from me . . . "

"You thought bloody right," said Cass. "You're another man's wife, for Christ's sakes. You said you had only been with two men."

"I have. I have."

"But . . . "

"There was someone, just after leaving school, and then there was Simon."

Simon. There was a name now, to add to his nightmares. A husband called Simon. Soon she would be telling him what Simon looked like, showing him a photograph, asking him what he thought of Simon's looks.

"So you're Mrs Williams."

"No. No, Williams is *my* name. His is Pentle. Simon Pentle. He's a nice man, Cass."

"Don't tell me *that*. I've got enough to think about as it is. Here I am, in love with another man's wife, and you tell me he's *nice*. I don't want him to be nice. Tell me he's a bastard. Tell me he drinks heavily and beats you with his fists afterwards. Tell me you hate his guts."

She took his face in her hands, holding it so that he would look into her eyes.

"I've lied enough. He isn't a bad man, Cass, but I like you better. I love you, better."

"Well, what happened? Was it a bad marriage?"

"What happened was I fell in love with you, that's all there is to it. Oh, we weren't close, not in the way a couple should be. We'd agreed that while I was over here, both he and I could date others. It was all above board, Cass, really. He works in London – a barrister. We have our own careers. We've only lived together in the same house for a few months . . . "

Cass put his hands over his ears.

"Stop it," he cried. "Just stop for a moment. Let me get this straight. You have an open marriage, right? You can go with other men, he can go with other women. Has it always been like that? I mean, from the start?"

"Yes, always," she replied. "We were never *in* love, we loved each other, but . . . "

"Look, that's just wordplay. The fact is, you didn't have a conventional marriage. I'm not interested in all that crap about

245

what kind of love it was. I'm basically concerned that I'm up to my neck in busting up a marriage."

"We needed each other at the time. I was . . . underconfident, insecure, so was Simon. We needed each other's support. Is that so hard to understand?"

"Not now you've explained it, it isn't. You just didn't want to face the world alone, so you teamed up with each other."

She nodded. "Something like that."

"Now you want to team up with me, but what about next year, or the year after?"

"Forever, Cass."

"I expect you said that to Simon. Some people deal in short forevers, Susanne."

"All right," she said quietly, "I'm not going to beg you, Cass. I'm here, if you want me, because I *do* love you, but don't make me crawl, please, because you'll feel awful about it later. I know you."

Cass managed to detach himself from her at last.

"But what about fidelity, Susanne? I mean, you and me? I can't live with someone who wants a loose relationship like the one you seem to have with your husband. I don't believe in those kinds of partnerships. If you start spending a lot of your time with someone else, like you did with me, you're bound to get fond of them. That's human nature."

"I don't fall in love with *everybody*."

"No, but the chances of meeting someone you can fall in love with, and *letting* yourself, are obviously much higher when you go out looking."

She said, "We won't be like that, Cass. It was like that with Simon and me because . . . because we were just fond of each other. There was no passion. I just *thought* I was in . . . "

Cass held up his hand, interrupting her.

"Don't say it, Susanne. Please, don't recant. You said you never did that. If you loved him once, you loved him. You didn't *think* it – you *did*. If you were my wife I would hate you for

246

wiping out something that existed, just because you want it out of your past."

"I want to be your wife, Cass."

"I have to go back and think about it. I do love you, you know that. But I can't trust you at the moment. I'll . . . see you later."

He kissed her on the cheek and she turned and went inside. Then he walked away, towards the hill. He felt very unhappy. The time was coming when they would be leaving Aden and the chances were that he and Susanne would not go to the same place. She would probably be sent back to England, while he would no doubt finish his tour in the Gulf: Bahrain, or Muscat and Oman. They really had to know how they stood before then.

42 Commando had arrived in Aden a few days before, to aid the final withdrawal. The terrorists of the NLF and FLOSY groups were now much more intent on killing each other than the British, though they were still taking time out to attack the infidel occasionally. Since the Six-Day War, Nasser had his hands full back in Cairo, so FLOSY were not getting a great deal of support from that direction. The NLF had had successes upcountry, deposing the sheiks, and looked to be the party that would come out on top. In the meantime, they were each kicking open doors and mowing down the other with little discrimination. In certain areas of Aden, not just the desert border beyond Sheik Othman, Arabs were carrying arms openly.

To Cass, it seemed a mess. There was Blue 16, lying dead in some dusty grave in Silent Valley, while his murderers not only went unpunished, they would likely dance on his grave once the British had gone. It certainly did not look as if the Federation was going to be running things, and though the British seemed to have remained in Aden for the past year simply to put the sheiks in power, they had failed miserably. Cass was an inverted snob, wasn't he? Parkinson had accused him of such. It was true, he was a confirmed anti-aristocrat. What the hell was he doing here in the first place, helping to put in a royalist government? He supposed he should be glad that the communists looked likely to succeed the British, only he couldn't forgive them for all the killing they had done. Not just Blue 16 and other servicemen, but also schoolchildren, both Arab and British. Innocent women too. *Innocent*. What did that word mean, anyway? When a state was as torn as Aden, one had to take sides. There was no neutral ground. The mutiny had shown what side most of the Arabs were on, and the uniforms they wore in no way reflected their loyalties. Why should they? Only a fool would be loyal to the British at this stage of their colonial rule.

Cass had heard some of the wives, before they were evacuated, talking about their servants. They said things like, "Mohammed has been with me for six years. I would trust him with my life. He's as loyal as a puppy." Those wives had about as much sense as puppies themselves. Mohammed, if his future was to be long and healthy, would certainly be as loyal as a dog, but not to the British woman who would go back to England in a couple of months' time and leave him to face inquisition by the NLF. She would be having tea and crumpets in the Granchester Copper Kettle, talking about the quality of British Home Stores' knickers, while Mohammed was being put up against a wall before a firing squad, for being the loyal servant of a woman who had paid him two pounds a week to do her housework for her. Would he? Not likely. He would take the much more sensible course of offering to stick a bomb under the dining-room table while the memsahib entertained her friends at one of her famous coffee mornings.

Still, he, Cass, couldn't forgive the killing, whatever the motives. It sickened him. Only the evening before he had seen an Arab and his young son, laughing and joking as they went out through the main gate of the camp in a small car. Two minutes later there was an explosion and Cass, along with others, went out in a Land-Rover to investigate. They found the small car looking like a balloon. Someone had thrown a grenade in through the side window of the vehicle. The occupants were smeared over the interior.

When he had finally climbed the hill, and the stairs to the top

248

balcony, he found a messenger waiting by his bed, a soldier from
42 Commando. He was carrying a Browning machine gun and
had belts of ammunition slung over his shoulder like a Chindit.
There was a deep scowl on the man's face, as if he had been
waiting a long time. All along the balcony Cass could see faces
peering from beds at this heavily-armed warrior in their midst.
The closest the balcony's residents came to such armour was on
sentry duty, which would appear to be tame stuff when compared
with this soldier's duties. None of them had even seen a Browning
at such close quarters.

"You Corporal Carson? Flight Lieutenant Parkinson wants to
see you right away," said the soldier.

"Where?" Cass was desperately running the past few days'
events over in his mind. Had he done something wrong at the
section? Or maybe it was his family? His mother might be ill.
"Do you know what it's about?" he asked the messenger.

"He wants you down at the main gate. They've got some
gollies trapped in a schoolhouse over at Khormaksar. Come on,
mate, I don't want to miss any of the action."

The soldier, a thick-limbed man with a heavy forehead, led
the way back down the hill at a fast pace. Cass trotted on behind,
feeling insecure and inadequate. At the bottom of the hill another
figure stepped out of the shadows, and startled Cass, making him
exclaim, "Jesus!" and then look to the commando to see if it was
all right, because the man was a Bedu Arab, almost as loaded
down with weaponry as the soldier himself.

"Sir? This the bloke you want?" said the soldier to the Bedu.

The Bedu also scowled at Cass. In the light of the perimeter
lamps Cass could see unshaven cheek-stubble stained with *qat*
juice set in a dark creased face. There was a glint to the eyes
which Cass recognized, though he was incredulous.

"Sir? Flight Lieutenant Parkinson?"

"Ignore the get-up, Carson," said Parkinson. "I've just been
out in the desert. We've got the gulli-gulli man, over in the old

249

Khormaksar School. I want you to persuade him to come out, so we can get him alive. He's threatening a shoot-out."

Still Cass stared at the figure before him, dressed in dirty desert rags, crossed by bandoliers of ammunition, turbaned, smelling of camels and goatshit. He was a frightening figure, in the way that Cass's mother had been terrifying in her gypsy outfit, when he was a young boy. It seemed that certain people were able to change into what they *really* were, for brief periods, as if it were part of the life cycle of such creatures. Parkinson and his mother, they were strange supernatural faerie-folk who went about disguised as ordinary people most of the time, but just occasionally you caught them in their magical raiment and they made you swallow lumps of fear to pay for the privilege.

"Abdulla? In the school?" he repeated, stupidly.

"Yes . . . "

At that moment a Land-Rover pulled up beside them with a screech and Parkinson and the soldier jumped in.

"Come on, man," snapped the flight lieutenant, and Cass climbed up beside him.

The Land-Rover hurtled through the gateway and along the coast road to Khormaksar. They went through Maalla's Murder Mile in the dead of night: a thing Cass promised himself he would never do. Miraculously they came out the other side without being shot to pieces. After skirting Crater, they came to Khormaksar RAF camp. The school was close to the perimeter fence, where the main road ran between the old airmen's married quarters and the main part of the RAF station. Part of the fence was down, where a car had gone off the road and crashed through it and was holding it down. The occupants of the car seemed to be in the school, now surrounded by 42 Commando.

What we need here, thought Cass, *is the good old rock apes, to walk between the two parties with their bayonets fixed, to prevent more bloodshed.*

Facing each other, on either side of the schoolhouse wall, were two groups of professional killers: NLF fighters and 42

Commando soldiers. The rock apes were children compared with the people here tonight.

Floodlights lit the outer walls of the school. It was the first time since the trip from the airport on arrival in Aden that Cass had seen his old school again. A pang went through him. It looked much the same, apart from the pockmarked plaster where the commandos had fired their automatics into it.

Parkinson explained to him.

"There are three men in the school, one of them is Abdulla Achmed. A fourth one is up there . . . " Parkinson pointed with his Bedu's forefinger at the roof of the school. Cass could see barbed wire running around the roof's parapet, and draped over this was a life-size rag doll: something that used to be a man. Even as he spoke, the air became charged with gunfire. Those in the school had loosed a few shots, while the commandos let go with ear-shattering automatic volleys that ripped into the plaster walls, filling the night with white dust. Just as Cass had decided to duck down behind the Land-Rover, it was all over, as abruptly as it had begun, without any orders or exchange of words, as if everyone knew exactly how many shots to fire at any given moment in the whole history of this particular event.

Parkinson then took a megaphone.

"I'm going to tell him you're out here," he said, "and that he can surrender to you. You said he was your friend. If you're telling the truth, then he'll save face by coming out for you."

Cass was not sure this would work at all.

"Why would he want to surrender to a corporal, when there's all these officers around?"

"I've told you, to save face. The gulli-gulli man has always said he'll never be taken alive by the British forces. You were his boyhood friend, it might make all the difference. I want to give it a try, anyway. Talk to him, if he wants you to."

The windows of his old school looked black and depthless, as if a whole universe lay behind them: a universe of nefarious mysteries. Was Abdulla in there? The Abdulla of his childhood?

251

Cass could only picture him as a lean smiling boy, not as the man he would be now. If he tried to think of him as an adult, the result was a giant Ché Guevara whose stature dwarfed all those around him; whose face held the wisdom of a hunted man; whose eyes, hard as flint, recognized no school chums with white faces. This was not a picture of the Abdulla he knew.

Cass was unhappy, but said, "Okay, I'll do it."

Parkinson stared at him.

"You weren't being asked," said the flight lieutenant, "you were being told," and raised the megaphone to his lips.

25

Dix was vomiting and scaring me with the sound. It seemed like he was bringing up the lining of his stomach, he was retching so much. The noon sun was pounding down on us and all our water was now gone. I didn't feel sick, like Dix, but my head was raging with pain. I just wanted someone to come and chop it off, get rid of it somewhere, so that I could have some rest from the torment.

We had started walking again, we didn't even care in what direction any more, but it was probably east. It was better than just lying, waiting for something to happen. My tongue felt like a puff adder in my mouth and my throat ached. That tantalizing bottle of lemonade had gone from my mind, and in its place were prayers. I had never prayed so hard in my life, hoping for someone to appear on the horizon, or for the air to have a salt smell to it. God must have been busy that day, listening to me saying please, please, please. I made him a lot of promises as well; some I knew I would never be able to keep, but then he knew that too.

"You all right?" I asked Dix in a thick voice.

"*Urrrggh* – yeah, think so."

We stumbled on. The sun was big and round, filling the sky. I kept thinking it was getting closer to the earth, that it was actually falling on our heads. One part of me knew this was not so, but every so often I felt the inclination to duck and wait for the impact. I mentioned it to Dix, but he didn't reply. His eyes looked small in his head and his mouth hung open all the time now.

Something like an hour later a figure appeared on a hill. We shouted and yelled, waving our arms, not caring if it was a Bedu or a tribesman out for blood. All we knew was that the figure must have known where it was, in what direction lay the sea, and would have access at least to drinking water. We started a sort of stumbling run, screaming hoarsely as we did so, but before we had gone ten yards the figure had disappeared. Nevertheless, we went on to climb the rise. I suppose we were both thinking that behind that hill perhaps there was a town, with everything we needed at our fingertips.

I scrambled up the slope, using my hands as well as my feet, careless of scorpions or anything else that might have been in the scree. It couldn't have taken us more than a quarter of an hour to reach the summit of the small rise, but once there we both sat down and cried. The man – if it was a man – had gone. The landscape behind the hill matched the wasteland over which we had already trudged. There was no town. There was not even a hut. I could see a kind of goat track in the dust, but it disappeared into the desert at the foot of the slope. There was nothing to follow, nor any point to head for which looked hopeful.

Once we were down, we lay where we were and I alternately dozed and gazed out at the heat waves rippling all round us, distorting the true shape of the terrain. My feet and hands were cut now, though not deeply. My headache subsided into a dull heavy weight inside my skull. The worst was my throat, which felt raw enough to be bleeding. I started to let the hope drain from me into the dusty rocky ground. Lizards, normally shy creatures, came out of their hiding-places now and darted up to us, looking at us directly, as if we were food. Even when I shooed them away, they didn't go far, but turned and looked back. At least there were no buzzards circling us: none that I could see, anyway.

I began to dream about my family.

My mother was out on the veranda, sweeping up the dust with one of those "witch's broom" brushes which the sweep-boys used. The dust was blacker, occasionally redder, than I remembered it. Gradually her piles of dirt got bigger, but the floor became no cleaner. Then I realized it was flowing with dirt like water, washing back and forth like a place in flood. There were thousands of tiny white eggs around the edge of the movement, that kept hatching into black or red specks of dust. Then I knew that the motes were not dirt, but ants. Some of them were living, some dead, some dying. It was the dead ones that she swept into the piles. However fast she cleared the corpses, more appeared in their place. While she swept quickly, her thin arms going ten to the dozen to get rid of the dead ants, thousands more live ones poured out of cracks in the wall and from the eggs around the edge of the veranda, and fought furiously with each other, to keep up the body count.

Dad came out on to the veranda and though none of them touched Mum, the ants flowed over him and quickly engulfed him. He was black and red, from head to toe, like a walking silhouette. When he opened his mouth below his sightless eyes, the ants poured in and down his throat. Instead of panicking, trying to brush them off, he treated them as if they weren't there, telling Mum he was on his way to work and would be home at half past one. Then he strolled off along the roadway, towards the camp gates, a black phantom dripping live ants in his wake. People stopped to stare at him, but he treated them as if they were silly in the head and even turned to Mum and touched his temple with his forefinger, then pointed to the bystanders.

Duggy and Richie came out next, with their schoolbags, and the ants flowed up their legs, up into the holes of their short trousers. They too seemed not to notice.

Then I came out, terrified that the ants were going to smother me, and as I stepped into their agitated masses they seemed to boil around my feet, as if just waiting for the word to flow up my legs. I took one or two gingerly steps towards the edge of the veranda, towards the clean sand beyond. Mum told me not to be so stupid, that they were only ants and wouldn't hurt me.

"You great nancy," she said, leaning on her brush, "what are you frightened of? They're not going to eat you."

"I don't like them," I cried, "they kill each other."

"Look at your brothers, they don't mind," she said, and when I turned, there were just black-and-red blobs behind me and I could see the ants biting furiously at the flesh beneath. My feet felt as if they were concrete blocks and I couldn't run.

I screamed as the black and red rivers flowed towards me. As they began biting into me, finding every orifice in my body, I heard my mum say, "Have you washed *properly* behind your ears this morning – you could grow potatoes."

"Yes," I screamed. "Yes, yes, yes."

"Huh," she sniffed, folding back an ear covered in ants, "a lick and a promise, as usual."

When I woke, the sun was going down. Dix was lying half across my legs. My chest ached and my mouth felt cracked and raw. I tried to go to sleep again, but I just remained groggy. When I sat up, one or two ants fell off my shirt.

Dix opened his eyes as I moved, and he too pulled himself up and tried to get to his feet. Without saying anything, we began walking in the opposite direction to the sun. We left the backpacks where we had been sleeping, but that was purely because we hadn't the energy to pick them up. Those parts of my skin which had been exposed to the sun were red and blistered, even though I had a deep tan. When I looked at Dix and saw what a ghastly mess his face was in, I knew how I looked myself.

When the light left us, we carried on. It must have been about eight o'clock when we heard the waves and smelled the salt in the air. Dix started running – a kind of wobbly jog – and I was close behind him. A few minutes later there was a shining mass of water before us, lying under the starlight, but the shoreline

256

was rock with no sandy beach. Dix went up to one of the bright still rock pools that waited with ghostly patience for the return of the tide, and he went down on his knees and began to drink. A few moments later he was retching again, this time bringing up a thin slime from somewhere. I didn't try to drink, because I have an aversion to salt, even sprinkled on my food. I knew it would do me absolutely no good whatsoever to drink from the sea.

"We could try strainin' some through our shirts," I said to Dix, who was still heaving, but he shook his head furiously.

"Won't work, I don't think."

Nevertheless, when he was able, we attempted the task, but the first drop of water made my cut lips sting so violently that I woke up properly for the first time that day. It was obvious after a couple of sips that we weren't going to get the salt out of the water that way. This inability to strain the sea frustrated me. I couldn't get the idea of ordinary table salt out of my mind. It seemed to me that salt was like fine grit or sand and should behave accordingly. I had a vast gap in my knowledge of chemistry that would not be closed until I went to military school.

"We have to move on," said Dix, "till we come to a beach. Then we can dig for fresh water in the sand."

So we began to walk again, but the rocky coastline was much harder to traverse than the desert, and our energy levels were almost at zero. We had not eaten or drunk anything for many hours now and our systems began to show it with a lack of co-ordination and a loss of perception in various areas. The waves would be roaring one moment and fade away into the distance the next. I bent my will to finding a sandy beach with a tidemark. I believed then that concentration was the key to success. If you centred on something strongly enough, you could make it happen. You made your own luck that way. In tennis, if I concentrated on getting the ball back to the baseline, hard and fast, I was usually successful. When I was running, if I concentrated on crossing the line first, it usually happened that way. Therefore, such a thing was a law of nature, and extended to all aspects of the universe. It did not occur to me that in one situation I was directing the action and in the other the action was directing me. Instead of setting out to find the beach, I was asking the beach to find *us*.

"At least we know we're heading the right way," I said to Dix, stumbling alongside him.

He was more pragmatic than me.

"We'll never make it! We'll run out of steam."

I knew that was true. Someone had to find us. I thought Skip and the others would have called out the rescue service by now, and they would have MTB launches going up and down the coast, and helicopters over the desert. There would be search parties as numerous as ants, all crawling over the landscape looking for us. Why hadn't they found us? Why hadn't they come across us? Why didn't God lead them to us?

By ten o'clock we were hardly moving, we were so exhausted. The rocky shoreline seemed to go on for ever into the darkness. I tried scratching away the soil at the top of the shore, but knew in my heart that the water would be too far down for us to reach without proper tools, perhaps even with them. We lay down on the flat rocks worn smooth by the waves and let the spray cool us, without drinking any down. I lay and stared at the stars. They looked cold, like chips of ice.

Dix said, "We're going to die, Cass ... " but I couldn't contemplate such a thing, even at that stage. You didn't just die of nothing. Someone had to do something to you, or you caught an illness which did it for you. A man had to shoot you, or stab you, or you fell from a cliff, or polio paralysed your heart, something *definite*. Dying was not something I could associate with lying on a rock cooling my fever in the mist of the ocean. You couldn't get sprayed to death. Something had to whack you hard in the head or heart to kill you.

"No," I replied. "No, we're not."

I think he misunderstood my feelings and believed it was determination in the face of impossible odds that made me argue

258

with him. I think he believed I was stiffening my upper lip, straightening my spine and saying that I was prepared to rage at the dying of the light.

He said, "You're a bloody marvel, Cass."

In truth, I just didn't think we were going to die. I had my eye on the horizon for the figure of Skip, or my dad, or some search party that would save us. It was stupidity that made me say such a thing, not courage in the face of adversity.

It strikes me now that we were both at peculiar polarities for our natures. A strong imagination has made me into a coward where death is concerned. I have died of cancer many times. I have had my brains blown out by a fanatical terrorist more than once. I have fallen from cliffs and been hung by the neck until my tongue lolls long and heavy, and my eyes poke out of my skull. The scenarios are familiar to me. In my nightmares and my daymares I have been the victim of disease and violence many many times. I blame an obsessive nature and a deep imagination for these deaths, which Dix would never have considered in the ordinary way of things.

Yet, here we were, on the edge of life, and taking opposite stands. Dix was seeing death and I was seeing rescue. He, I suppose, was looking at truth, while I was still staring into that inner well of imagination, it working *for* me for once, instead of against me.

The night hours went by and we slept restlessly, our brains ragged and our bodies craving liquid. I think both of us were a little addled by that time and had begun to talk nonsense.

When the sun began to creep over the sea I climbed unsteadily to my feet.

"Walk," I croaked, not wanting to lie in one spot any longer.

Dix said, "Stayin' here." He didn't even open his eyes.

I didn't know what to do. I didn't want to go on alone, leave him there, but the idea of just drying up into a husk on the rock was totally abhorrent to me.

The decision would not come.

259

I stood and swayed over his prone form, cursing him with all the swearwords I knew, but he didn't move a muscle.

Just then, I saw a figure, standing on a rise and looking down on us.

It was an Arab.

"Dix, Dix!"

"Go away, Cass," he moaned.

"No, Dix, someone's come . . . "

He lifted his head and I pointed.

The figure had begun walking towards us.

Dix sat up, staring.

At first I didn't recognize him under his headdress, but as he came closer the stride of the man seemed familiar to me. In fact it wasn't a man – not a fully grown man – but a youth like ourselves. The dust formed little clouds around his feet, as his bare soles hit the ground. He strode up to us, stopping about five yards away. His face was rigid, unsmiling, but somehow full of triumph.

"Abdulla," I said weakly.

His hands were on his hips.

"I said I would find you, and I *did*!" he cried fiercely, and took off his headdress, and threw it hard into the dust at his feet. "I said I would, and I did."

"My *very* good friend," I said.

Then he laughed. The joy in that laughter was genuine, totally sincere, and I remember its sound today, though I've never heard any feeling expressed so clearly since. We threw our arms around each other and hugged. Dix laughed too: a choking, sore-throated laugh. He shook hands gravely with Abdulla.

"Well done," he said, "you've saved us." He looked at Abdulla's empty hands. "You've got some water, haven't you?"

A tragic expression suddenly took the place of the grin on Abdulla's features. He stepped back and gave a little gasp. Dix dropped to his knees and I could see he was about to cry. I had a lump in my throat as big as an egg and I wanted to cough it

260

up, but could not do so without fluid and my spittle had dried to a crust in my mouth.

Then Abdulla flicked a speck of dust from his shirtfront with his left hand, and when I next looked at his right hand, there was a goatskin in it, which had appeared as if by magic. He shook the skin, grinning at the same time, and we heard the splosh of water.

"You bugger, Abdulla," laughed Dix, getting up off his knees, "you bloody bugger!"

Abdulla left us half an hour later and returned at noon with a group of people which included Skip. They had a radio transmitter with them and called for a launch, which arrived not long after.

We were taken home.

26

Said came into my bedroom looking very shy. He gazed at me and shook his head sorrowfully, before lifting his right arm and showing me what he had in his hand. It was his African thorn-tree stick, with its wonderful carvings of snakes and hyenas and strange trees. I knew what he intended to do, straight away, and I felt tremendously embarrassed for some reason, as if I'd interrupted his prayers at a crucial moment. He held out the magic staff.

"You keep this. No more get lost," he said.

I was overwhelmed by the gesture. I might have begun by refusing if I hadn't known that this would be very insulting to him. Said and his people did not offer something unless they intended you to have it. To refuse it would be taken to mean that I thought the gift was not good enough for me. So I thanked him profusely, saying it was the most wonderful present I had ever had, and that I would treasure it for ever. He just smiled his skull-like smile, the veins standing out on his brow in ridges. "This never mind," he said. "Great-grandfather stick keep safe now."

Then he left my room.

Later, as I lay in bed wondering if at some time I should try to give the stick back to Said, since it was a family heirloom, or whether he would still be insulted if I did, my mother came in smiling like a winged messenger with good news from the Lord.

262

"You've got a visitor," she said.

"Who?"

"Wait and see, she'll be up in a minute," and I knew then that Heather was in my house – *in my house* – and was coming up to *my* bedroom. I smoothed down the sheets, propped myself up on pillows and began to feel self-conscious about my skinny chest. She had seen the monstrosity before, of course, when we had gone swimming together, but somehow my chest in bed looked thinner than my chest in the swimming pool. I wished I could pump it up, with a bike pump or something, and expand it before she entered the room.

When she came in, bearing a box of chocolates, she proved to be as shy as I was myself.

Heather sat down primly on the straight-backed chair provided by my mother. She was wearing a gingham dress with a white collar, white socks and neat black shoes. As always, she was well groomed and shining from soap and water. Her cheeks had a healthy Scottish glow to them. Those Kilmarnock eyes, with their wild-shore greys and sea-blown-sky blues, were Scotland itself.

"How are you feeling, Cass?"

My mother discreetly left the room.

"I'm fine now. A bit ill yesterday."

"I'm sure you were. We were so worried about you . . . I've brought you some chocolates."

"Thanks. Do I share them with Dix, or has he got his own?"

"I've got some more to give to him."

That was all I wanted to know. She had come to see me *first*.

She stood up then and walked to the end of the bed, to look out at the desert through the open window. I sat up higher in the bed, trying to see what she was staring at, but there was nothing except sand and dust and rock out there.

"Did you have a really bad time?" she asked. "I cried, you know. And I prayed for you. I thought you were both . . . you know. When I go away from here at the end of the month, we shall probably never see each other again – probably – and I

263

want to know – did you think of me at all, when you were out there?"

"Quite a lot," I mumbled, not really knowing how to handle this interview.

She turned and looked me full in the eyes. She looked as serious as I'd ever seen her.

"Quite a lot?"

"Most of the time," I said. "Quite a lot of most of the time, because . . . I don't know why. I just did."

"I know why," she said, and smiled the way she had done in Sheik Othman Gardens, "but you're not supposed to say, because you're just a boy still, and boys don't, do they?"

"No," I said, getting out of my depth again, "they're not supposed to."

She didn't stay long, but when she did get up to leave, she kissed me on my cheek.

"I think you're super," she said, "so take care. See you back at school."

"Yeah," I said, blushing furiously, "see you back at school."

Inside I felt like Christmas holidays.

My family treated me as if I were made of thin glass for about three days, then their unnatural patience ran out and we went back to normal. I was allowed to get up and walk around, which I could have done at least a day earlier, and play some board games with the rest of them, instead of hearing the dice being thrown and the cards slapped down, and feeling out of it all.

"Back to school next week," said my mother.

"How's Dix?" I asked her.

"All right," she sniffed. "He's putting about the story that he was the one that held it all together. That you would have died if it wasn't for him."

That didn't sound like Dix at all.

"His mum said it, didn't she?"

Mum looked up and then nodded.

"And you've been saying the opposite."

She looked taken aback.

"Now don't get cheeky with me, young man!"

I left it there, knowing that the two mums had been waging a propaganda war in the wake of the incident. This was natural cause-and-effect. Mums did that sort of thing to get rid of the steam. The two of them had spent two anxious days waiting for news of us, going through all sorts of hell swaying back and forth between imagining the worst and being hopeful for the best. Apparently some rags had been found at the foot of a cliff and taken home to be identified. When they were shown to my mother, she had burst into tears, shaking herself in relief. They had radioed ahead, telling her they had found some clothes that might be mine. Dix's mum had gone through the same thing. There was a lot of pressure inside them and they had to get rid of the stress somehow. A good battle over whose son was the hero and whose the dependant was a satisfactory method of opening a few valves and letting it hiss harmlessly into the atmosphere.

Back at school, we were both heroes. The Gophner twins let us have a go on their roulette wheel for nothing, and didn't squeal when we won a few clear green alleys, though they drew the line at rainbow marbles and quarter-inch ball bearings. One of the girls offered to buy me an ice-cream, but I knew it would upset Heather, so I said no thank you very much. Dix talked to Mr Cootley quite a bit, and since he didn't like me much, I was left to chat to Ma Gower, who did.

We basked for a few days in the glamour.

My dad wanted to reward Abdulla – in fact everyone did – but he would accept nothing. He said it would make it seem as if he had done it for money, when we knew it was for friendship. I told him not to be daft, to take the money and run, because *we* (the important people) knew why he had come to search for us, what did it matter what anyone else thought? He said, no, it would make it a cheap thing, not worth keeping in his heart, if they gave him something as if he had done a job for them. So, the act remained pure, untainted by gain.

The time came when Heather was to board the SS *Devonshire* and return to Scotland.

My parents said I would soon get over her.

(What lies they told us when we were young!)

We spent the last evening on her veranda, plotting to stow away in her ship. It would not have taken much for us to carry that out, but the thought of being separated after going through such an ordeal, probably prevented it. There was no hope in it.

"Goodbye Dixie." She kissed him on the cheek, so I knew what was coming for my turn, and prepared myself.

"Goodbye Cass." I moved at the last second and kissed her full on the lips. Her eyes widened in surprise, then crinkled a little, and I knew that if we had all not been feeling so sad, she would have smiled, knowingly. It was the only time in our relationship that I felt I was in control.

"Goodbye Heather."

"Goodbye Heather."

She turned and went straight indoors.

As we walked away, into the night, I could still taste the salt from her lips. I can taste it now.

The wonderful thing about a friendship that's been terminated by circumstances beyond the control of both people, is that it's preserved in amber. It can never be changed.

It is what it was, for ever.

A month later, Dix left Aden. We shook hands, stiffly, friends and rivals to the bitter end.

Two days after Dix had sailed, I received my first letter, the first of a great many over the years, from Heather. It was in answer to one I had written to her a week after she had gone.

266

Dear Cass,

I was really delighted in finding your letter waiting for me at lunch time, for I had just come home from school after a rotten morning of French and Maths, etc. I have something to confess, Cass. I thought you wouldn't write to me, so you can just imagine how glad I was to get your letter and I'm truly sorry for thinking such a thing. I started school last week and love it as I'm in the same class as most of my old friends. On the whole I'm quite pleased to be back home as the weather has been wonderful. But of course I miss Aden for a lot of things (you very much included). I have just seen "Young at Heart" at the cinema, oh! you must see it, it's really great. Gill wrote me a letter and in it she said you were a wretch and a strict anti-girl male (I'm quite glad to hear it, I mean the anti-girl part) she also said Lucy Huggins still gazes at you rapturously from across the room. (She also said you said Lucy makes you sick. I actually had the bad manners to laugh.) From what I hear your legs must have muscles like rocks with all the walking you do, and I'm glad you enjoyed your last scout camp. When I went back to school Tam Adams stopped to speak to me (but there's nothing to fear as he's just the same old mad Tam). I also met a very nice boy on the ship called Terry, well he sent me a very nice letter not long ago. Really Cass, I'm not trying to make you jealous, but it's only because I want you to know everything that happens. All our deep-sea trunks have arrived, but the record player is broken, so your dear Eddie Cantor won't be groaning for some time. Well, Cass, I must close, so give my kindest thoughts to your family.

Love,
Heather

PS Terry doesn't hold a candle to *you*.

267

I was ecstatic at receiving such a letter from her. In it she had told me more about her feelings than she had done in all our time together. I took the mention of the two boys with a pinch of salt. There was a tiny streak, a thin line really, of love-cruelty in her which caused her to prick me, occasionally, to a jealous reaction, but that only made her human so far as I was concerned. Who wants to be in love with an angel? She wrote me such letters (though they improved in style and grammar) until her early twenties, when they suddenly stopped, and mail to her old address was returned to me stamped "Not known at this location". It was almost as if a prince had descended on her household and whisked her away, which is what I expect must have happened.

Dix wrote once or twice, but we soon gave that up. We had nothing to say to each other that could not be relayed more effectively by Heather, so that's how we got each other's news, through her. He eventually went to Cardiff University, then naval college and became a radio communications officer: something he had talked about in Aden as a boy. The fact that we used Heather as a relay station helped to maintain the myth that we were still all good friends together, and not three strangers separated by time.

27

Parkinson had been talking in Arabic through the megaphone, to the occupants of the schoolhouse. He now handed the instrument to Cass. He was no longer the friendly flight lieutenant towards whom Cass had warmed when they conversed during odd moments at the radio shack. He was a hard-bitten intelligence officer, whose prime interest was obtaining information.

"Tell him you're out here," said Parkinson.

Cass replied, "I don't know that much Arabic."

"He speaks English, you know he does. Just explain to him who you are and what you're doing here."

Cass lifted the megaphone to his mouth.

"Abdulla," he shouted, surprised at the distorted sound of his own voice, "this is Cass. You remember me? You saved my life once, when we were boys. I got your Uncle Hussein a job. Cass and Dix, and Heather? You must remember. We were all good friends once." He was suddenly aware of the officer beside him in fancy dress and he wanted to tell him and his men to go away, while he spoke with his old friend, but that was of course impossible.

"Listen, Abdulla, I don't like getting mixed up between you and the army. I'm here because I've been ordered to ask you to surrender. It's not what I want to do. I didn't even want to come back to Aden, not now it's been torn apart, but I had to. They made me. Anyway, what they want is for you to come out, to surrender yourself to me, because we were once good friends. Can you hear me, Abdulla?"

He lowered the megaphone and Parkinson gripped his wrist.

"Let him think about it," said the flight lieutenant.

Cass looked at the commandos around him, all grim-faced, probably longing for a showdown with this terrorist who had been responsible for the deaths of *their* comrades. Most of the soldiers present just wanted to shoot holes into the "gollies" inside the school, because that was what they were trained to do, and it was more satisfying than taking the enemy alive. Prisoners would walk out of jail one day. Dead men couldn't climb out of their graves.

He trusted that Parkinson would keep Abdulla alive though, because the officer wanted the gulli-gulli man for his own purposes. No doubt there was information to be had from such high-ranking terrorists as Abdulla? Or maybe they wanted to persuade him to identify other NLF members? It didn't matter to Cass, so long as his words were not betrayed.

Parkinson said in a low voice, "Laying it on a bit thick, aren't we? *Ordered* to come here? What about duty, and queen and country, and all that sort of thing?"

Cass couldn't tell whether Parkinson was being cynical or not.

"Which country are you talking about? Aden or England?"

"Smart little bugger, Carson," murmured Parkinson, staring at the school through the nightglasses.

Cass sighed, "Not smart. Not smart at all. If I was, I wouldn't be here. I've been used tonight. I've had enough – sir."

"Have you now?"

Cass didn't answer. He knew it was a futile argument. He'd never spoken to an officer in this way before and he knew that though he could get away with it because they needed him for the moment, once the moment was over Parkinson would probably come down on him like a ton of bricks. Of course, if the flight lieutenant got what he wanted out of this night's events, there would probably be no more said, so Cass decided to let things rest. It was pointless making trouble for himself, simply because he was depressed.

There was a shout from the schoolhouse.

"Cass? That is you?"

Cass did not recognize the voice. It was a man's voice, not a boy's. But he felt something in the tone, a familiar warmth. He responded to it eagerly.

"Yes, it's me."

"Ah, my very good friend . . . "

Yes, it was Abdulla.

" . . . you should not be here to watch me die."

"You don't need to die, Abdulla," cried Cass, without the megaphone now. "If you come out now, they won't shoot you. They've promised me that. I think I trust them."

"*Think?*" hissed Parkinson, beside him.

Abdulla's voice came again through the night.

"Ah, but can you trust *me*, my friend?"

"I don't know," said Cass, honestly.

There was silence for a while after that. Cass stared up at the heavens, wishing himself elsewhere. He saw a shooting star fall down the face of the sky, just as he had seen them as a boy. He remembered how they went to the open-air cinema, he and Dix and Abdulla, and when the film was a boring one, how they would lean back in their seats and study the constellations. He used to picture Heather's face in the stars. God, how he had missed her at first, after she had left Aden. Where was she now? Perhaps with Dix? Maybe they had met and secretly married behind his back, knowing the shock of their betrayal would be too much for him to bear? Why couldn't women have two husbands? Then they could send for him, to join them, and they would all be together again, just as it should be, just as it was in the lost days of innocence.

There was a shout from the school.

"What is it?" said Cass.

Parkinson replied, "He's coming out."

For a while nothing happened. The lights trained on the schoolhouse had clouds of motes caught in their beams and the shining dust seemed to emphasize the silence. There was a religious atmosphere to the scene. Perhaps the Reverend Griffith would suddenly appear to condemn them all as sinners? His church was not far away. He could have been on the spot in a few minutes, roaring and gesticulating, bringing with him the wrath of God gathered in the folds of his surplice. Once here, he could shake it out, on white and brown alike, bringing them all to justice. The Welsh padre had always said the spirit was stronger than the flesh. Even if Rev Griff's body was not in Aden, his spirit must have been.

A figure stepped slowly into the open doorway of the school. The lights were intensified, trained on this silhouette, which shielded its eyes with one arm. Cass could see illuminated by the brilliance of this new clutch of lamps, the place on the wall by the door where his initials had once been scrawled. They were no longer there, obliterated by several layers of whitewash.

The man moved forward, still holding his arm across his face. Was this tall muscled figure indeed Abdulla? He looked like any other Arab. There was nothing special about his dress – a *futa* kilt, a dark shirt, a skullcap – and his feet were bare. Surely a high-ranking terrorist should look imposing?

Parkinson barked an order and Abdulla looked to where the sound came from.

"Cass?" called the Arab.

"Here," he replied. "Over here, Abdulla."

Cass was suddenly very excited at being about to meet his friend again, after all those years. He was actually going to talk with Abdulla, exchange old confidences, remember times gone by. They could chat about Dix and *Heather*, bring them alive again in the place where they had had so many happy times together. At last, at last, someone who knew Heather, someone who could reinforce the memories, flesh out the ghosts.

The figure dropped his arm from his face. He walked slowly towards the spot where Cass and Parkinson stood. When he was about ten yards away, he stopped, stood still.

"Cass?"

"Yes, here. I'm standing with Flight Lieutenant Parkinson."

"Ah," said Abdulla, "Parkinson."

A slight gesture came from the figure, like the casual swatting of a fly on a shirtfront. A small movement. Insignificant. There was something which Cass recognized in the pose that followed. He had seen it many times before, in a boy who was good at conjuring tricks. Abdulla had tried to teach him, Cass, the same sleight of hand, but the British boy had never mastered it.

"NO!" yelled Cass.

But it was too late. The pistol had appeared in the gulli-gulli man's hands, as if by magic, perhaps from somewhere in the folds of his *futa*. The Arab managed to pull the trigger once, before the commandos opened fire and gutted him like a catfish. Abdulla's body hit the dust, seemed to bounce, and lay face down and crooked.

Cass was horrified. He felt stunned. The person on the ground was absolutely still. There was little doubt he was dead, his torso torn open by automatic fire. Then a flame of fear burned Cass's stomach. Had he been hit himself? Was he bleeding without being able to feel the pain, the shock having numbed him? He hastily inspected himself, wondering whether he would know if he'd been hit. Then he looked up at Parkinson, who had gone pale.

"Are you wounded, sir?"

"No. The round went between us," said Parkinson. "Damn! The bugger got what he wanted, after all. Dead as a doornail. Pity about that."

"He's not a bugger . . . " began Cass, but then more shooting came from the schoolhouse, as Abdulla's comrades began firing indiscriminately at the commandos surrounding them. Cass and Parkinson ducked behind the Land-Rover. The soldiers opened up with their weapons and the night was full of sound.

Parkinson said, "Here," and offered Cass a rifle from the back of the vehicle.

Cass shook his head.

"I've had enough of this."

"Don't be stupid, man. You're a corporal in the RAF. You're letting me down in front of the army."

"Fuck the army. I've got a schoolfriend lying dead over there. I lost another mate a few weeks ago. Fuck the army and fuck *you*." The words came spitting out. Cass could no longer contain his fury. His face felt hot and he was close to tears. He wanted to break something, smash something, punch Parkinson's face.

The officer loosed a couple of shots from a pistol, aiming carefully and coolly at the schoolhouse. He did not seem over-perturbed by Cass's anger, nor by his language. Any other officer would have threatened court martial for disobeying an order, insubordination, and a dozen other crimes. Instead, he turned to Cass and said, "Your schoolfriend just tried to kill you."

Cass shook his head violently this time.

"Not me – *you*."

"The shot went between us. We were less than a foot apart. Can you be sure he was aiming at me?"

"I'm sure."

Parkinson said, "You can't just give it up."

"Watch me," replied Cass.

When Cass was driven away in the Land-Rover by Parkinson, the men in the school were still there, still alive, still firing back occasionally. It would take a long while to get them out. The walls were solid and the army was not permitted to use anything bigger than a machine gun.

The sun came up behind Shamsan, filling the craggy hollows with light, the night leaving pieces of itself behind, beneath over-hangs and in caves and holes. The volcano was a dormant beast which would one day raise itself from the dust, shake out the sleepiness of millennia, and march out into the desert. Along the coastline, the boats began to stir.

"Had enough, eh?" murmured Parkinson, above the humming of tyres on asphalt. He said it as if he had been musing on the words for the past few hours.

"I've had enough," repeated Cass, mechanically, "I want to go home."

"Which home would that be, Aden or England?"

Cass declined to answer. He stared at the road ahead.

"Well, I'll tell you where you're going," said the officer, "and it's not to either of those places. The unit's pulling out tomorrow. You'll be in Bahrain by the end of the week. Satisfied?"

A mixture of feelings flooded into Cass. He felt glad, unhappy, relieved and fearful, all at the same time. Goodbye Aden, at last. And he still had not climbed Jebel Shamsan. Did that mean he would be back again, some time in the future? There was nothing here for him now: nothing at all. Heather and Dix were gone, Abdulla was dead. A place was people, wasn't it? At least, it needed people to make it special. Heather and Dix. He needed them now, very badly, to talk over what had happened to their childhood friend, Abdulla. He needed to ask them questions. *Had Abdulla really tried to kill him?* Questions that he couldn't answer on his own. *Had Abdulla changed, on growing to a man, completely? Was he so different that he was a stranger?* Questions that would torment him for a long time.

The shock of what had happened that night would not hit Cass until much later. One ordinary peaceful sunset he would be strolling down a gold-and-silver street in Bahrain, clutching the latest precious letter from Susanne, inspecting the filigree butter-flies and *jambia* brooches, the gemstones displayed in cracked tea saucers, the jewelled rings – when the cannon that signalled the end of a Ramadan day would go off, the sudden explosion making him dive to the ground automatically. The passers-by would stare at him, as he lifted himself from the street afterwards, and sheepishly brushed himself off. Then he would cross unsteadily to a darkening alley, and stand in its dying shadows, trembling and sweating alternately, finding the evening cool and warm both at once, his legs almost too weak to support him, and saying

275

to himself over and over again, "Abdulla's dead. Abdulla's dead . . . "

Parkinson said, "We forget tonight, understand? I don't want you to mention it to any of your pals. I'll put in a report, of course, but our own conversations will not be part of that report."

Cass nodded.

"Thanks."

He climbed out of the Land-Rover at the guardroom and walked along the road until he came to the nurses' quarters. Then he went round to a side window and tapped on the pane. After a few minutes the window opened and Susanne's face appeared.

"Cass?" she whispered, then obviously noticing his pallor, added, "What's wrong?"

"Are you on your own?" he asked.

She glanced back into her room.

"Yes. Judith's on duty."

"Can I come in?"

"Of course. Quickly, before someone sees you, or we'll both be in trouble."

He pulled himself up on to the windowsill and dropped into the room. Susanne was naked. She jumped back into bed and held open the single sheet which covered her. Cass took off all his clothes and climbed in beside her, holding her close to him. Then he turned his back to her and the pair of them curled naturally into a foetal position, she fitting into his curves perfectly, as if they were a matched pair of wooden figures.

"You're trembling," she said.

"I've had a bad time. My – one of my oldest friends was killed tonight . . . " The first tears came now, gentle tears for a young boy, from a young boy, "I saw – I saw . . . I'll – I'll tell you about it later. Now – now I just want you to hold me for a while."

She clutched him tightly, and began crying with him, for different reasons. There was much comfort to be had from just holding and being held.

276

28

I shook hands with Abdulla, wishing him goodbye and all the best, and thanked him again for saving my life. He was on his way upcountry, to some distant cousin's village where he was going to spend some time. It was something to do with a future wife, but he did not allow me into his private family concerns any further than saying, "Arrangements have been made and I must follow my father's wishes", and so we parted company, the best of friends. I watched him walk along the road towards Steamer Point and gave him a last wave and a shout, "I'll send some catfish to your uncle, next time I go fishing . . . " He acknowledged with a smile and quick flutter of his hand. By the time he returned to Aden, I would be on my way back to a strange land called England: a third-culture child, not Arabic, not wholly English.

Throughout my life I would meet others like me, men and women raised in Hong Kong, Singapore, Africa, Taiwan, all puzzled because they did not fit into the society that their parents settled back into quite comfortably, without any fuss. We would have something in common, these people and I, even though they might be French, or German, and raised in a foreign land I had never visited myself. There would be an affinity between us difficult, perhaps impossible, to define. There would be a warmth, a sharing of spirit, a feeling of familiarity. We would be outsiders for the rest of our lives, most of us taking to wandering the globe, looking for our childhoods. Sights and sounds and smells would be in us that meant nothing to our native countrymen.

Nights would be there, with different star patterns, different skies. Seasonal emotions quite foreign to home-grown men and women would spring up, blossom, and wither away annually, far from their source.

When I was nine or ten years old my father was ordered by my mother to tell me the facts of life. Mum then vacated the living room, leaving Dad looking as desperate as a man going to his own hanging. He began by mumbling about a husband and a wife sleeping in the same bed, something passing between them in the night, though he didn't say how or what, and ended with a dire warning which he inferred had to do with catching some awful disease:

"Remember, son, beware of painted ladies!"

I left the room knowing something important had happened in the way of family rituals, but confused as to what it all really meant. For years afterwards I had nightmares in which I was being attacked by giant butterflies.

The ship that took us from Aden saw the end of my sexual innocence.

By coincidence it was the SS *Devonshire*, the same ship that had the ghosts of Heather and a boy called Terry wafting about its decks. On the *Devonshire*, I shared a cabin with Slatt, a boy of my own age who had discovered sex. He was on his way home from Hong Kong and had already spent some weeks on board. During that time he had managed to bore a hole in the cabin wall so that he could peek through and watch the sixteen-year-old girl in the next cabin. The first night on board he invited me to watch her undress for bed, which I did, feeling old-fashioned wicked, and found tremendous stirrings going on in the lower regions of my body. My heart began to race too, not with love, but with something else I had no name for at the time.

The hole between the cabins was awkward to look through and we couldn't widen it for fear of discovery, so I hardly saw anything but a few wisps of underwear and some pale flesh. It was enough to reveal to me that there was a world of excitement that was only just coming into focus for me. The mind does more with a piece of lace and a patch of skin than it can do with a wholly nude woman in full view. It asks and answers its own questions and creates illusions from the flimsiest of evidence.

I began to experience wet dreams. It meant I had to wash my own pyjamas and dry them before giving them to Mum to wash again. In those days wet dreams were something to be ashamed of, outside the fraternity of male teenagers. Within the brother-hood, they were discussed with great seriousness and interest, as were the intimate parts of female forms, female underclothes and the size and naming of male parts. It was all very clinical most of the time, except when one had one's eye against the hole between the cabins, watching a pouting sixteen-year-old slip out of some-thing silky and into something silkier. Then it was a matter of genital pyrotechnics.

I used to study the girl outside the cabin, when she was eating in the dining room, amazed at the power she had over us. She liked to flirt with the stewards, who showed little interest for a reason I only understood a bit later in life, and the officers at the captain's table. A smooth-faced ship's officer, probably about twenty years of age, danced with her one entertainment evening and I never saw her eyes shine so brightly. I said we should invite him to the cabin for the night's performance behind the peephole, since he was obviously taken with her, but Slatt replied that the officer would probably be part of the show. At the time I wondered what he meant by that, and found out one shocking night just before we hove in to Port Sudan. She seemed such a nice girl too. She *was* a nice girl, apart from her pouting.

While on board ship for a long period, there is a suspension of reality. You find yourself caught in a sea of timelessness, which leaves the real world somewhere back in the mists of your past. Aden was a mythical land where I once dreamed I walked and worked and played with legendary people like Heather and Dix and Abdulla. Britain was even more remote. Britain was vague faces which belonged to grandmas and grandpas, ice and snow, green fields and rivers. That was it. At the time all of it, Aden and Britain, was fiction. I saw myself peeping through holes at girls for the rest of my life. That wasn't a bad future, so far as I was concerned, since I was terrified that one day I would have to actually *do* something with a girl. I caught up with the rest of youth with bang, not a whimper, at the age of seventeen. It was with a woman in her late twenties, to whom I shall always be grateful, against the back of a gravestone in a village churchyard. I suppose you could say it was a case of the quick amongst the dead.

One morning, the *Devonshire* arrived in Port Said, and who should come aboard but the gulli-gulli man. He was just as clever as ever, just as charismatic as he had been the first time I had seen him. He looked the same and did the same tricks. It felt as if nothing had really changed, no time had passed since I last saw him. His magic was timeless and he was an immortal. I found myself looking round for Dix, and Heather, so that we could talk animatedly about the magic in our lives. I wondered if they had seen him too, and had felt the same way as I was feeling at that moment. He made it seem as if time and distance weren't important any more.

Later the gulli-gulli man sailed away, in his little felucca full of magician's paraphernalia, his coloured silks, bronze cups, ribbons, birds and black canes, and left us young people behind.

Or maybe we went with him? Heather, Dix and I? Perhaps someone else stayed to grow into an adult in my place, to do the things that grown-ups have to do?